Astronomy with Binoculars

Astronomy
with Binoculars

JAMES MUIRDEN

D. VAN NOSTRAND COMPANY, INC.
Princeton, New Jersey
Toronto · London · New York

Printed in Great Britain
by Ebenezer Baylis and Son, Limited
The Trinity Press, Worcester, and London

FOR J.H.

Contents

Contents
LIST OF TABLES

Illustrations

PLATES

Contents

FIGURES

Contents

STAR MAPS

Foreword

Astronomy is an intimidating science, and the newcomer faces two hazards; first, the vast scale of everything; and, more immediately, lack of equipment. It is a reasonable but quite incorrect assumption to imagine that astronomical research can be conducted only in a big observatory, even though there is plenty of evidence to the contrary in the publications of the British Astronomical Association, the largest amateur society in the country.

This is partly due to a change of values. Much of astronomy has become a high-pressure business, linked in part with the onset of the Space Age; ideas are becoming more and more materialistic, and man's attitude to the universe is more practical than it was forty years ago when G. P. Serviss wrote his excellent little book *Astronomy With an Opera Glass*. This catered for the person who simply wanted an introduction to the night sky, and it would be a pity to pretend that anybody today looks at the stars without some feeling of humble inquiry. This book puts forward its own argument for the value of a pair of binoculars in this field; and if it fails the fault lies with me, not with the contention.

My thanks are due to Richard Dodd and John Larard for the binocular drawings of comet Seki-Lines and the Hyades star cluster, and I must also gratefully acknowledge the two beautiful drawings of auroræ by J. R. Bell. These, needless to say, were made with the naked eye alone; for I envisage the title of the book as a restriction, not a definition. It turns out, in actual fact, to be much less of a restriction than many people might think.

December, 1962   JAMES MUIRDEN

CHAPTER 1

Binoculars and Telescopes

During the past few years, with space-travel not merely round the corner but actually with us, popular astronomy has been given a record-breaking boost. Almost every week the newspapers announce some astronautical advance, and to cash in on this several manufacturers have mass-produced small, cheap telescopes. People buy them, gaze avidly at the Moon for a week or two, and then lose enthusiasm and leave them to collect dust in a corner. They do not realize that the password to amateur astronomy is 'patience'.

Today, amateurs need even more patience than ever before. Great telescopes are being built to probe regions far beyond the range of smaller instruments, and much work which was truly in the amateur department fifty years ago has been snatched away. Yet there is still a hard core left—the Moon, the brighter planets, and variable stars—which are well within the field of enthusiasts.

But not many people have telescopes which will even show a planet's disk, let alone detail on its surface. Does this mean that they cannot make any contribution at all to astronomy? The answer is an emphatic No. Telescopes are useless on auroræ; binoculars are ideal for observing bright comets; and the naked eye can see far more meteors than can be recorded by professional cameras, while it is also the best for observing fluctuations in the brightness of some of the brighter variable stars. All this work is, or can be, of real value.

Of course it is not necessary to do useful work to get

15

satisfaction out of astronomy. Simply watching the changing phases of the Moon, or the lethargic drift of the planets among the stars—best of all, perhaps, simply sweeping the Milky Way with low-powered binoculars; all these make us more intimately concerned with the workings of the universe. We all know that the Moon revolves around the Earth, but it is comforting to check up on successive nights just to make sure. We have seen photographs of the Milky Way which show far more stars than the finest telescope on the clearest night—but once again the second-hand can never match the real. The night sky is full of landmarks, and the best way to get on speaking terms with the stars is by using binoculars or a small telescope. Many amateurs, in fact, know the heavens far better than professional observers.

We do not have to search far for monuments to the humble amateur in present-day astronomy. To mention a department very much in the public eye, radio astronomy was born when an amateur casually noticed the connection between a recurrent hiss picked up by his radio set and the Earth's rotation. In 1901, and again in 1934, the heavens played host to two 'new stars', or novæ—stars which suddenly flare up in brightness. They were both discovered by amateurs, with nothing more vital than the naked eye. In 1956 a completely new meteor shower was observed by amateur observers in South Africa, and in 1959 George Alcock, a hard-working school-teacher, was rewarded for his hundreds of hours of patient comet-sweeping by the almost simultaneous discovery of two comets. And just to show that fate can be kind sometimes, Michael Candy, a professional astronomer, discovered a comet recently when testing a new telescope—by pointing it through a bedroom window! Much more recently, on 6 February 1963, the brightest nova for some years was discovered by a Swedish amateur, Elis Dahlgren, with the naked eye, and it was also found independently by an indefatigable comet hunter L. C. Peltier, of Ohio. We can expect further discoveries during the next decade.

The starting-point is a pair of binoculars or a small telescope, and they both work on the same basic principle (Fig. 1). Light from the object passes through the large convex lens, known as the 'object-glass', which bends or refracts the beam, making it converge to form an image. This image is then magnified by a much smaller lens, known as the 'eyepiece'. It is obvious that the larger the object-glass the more light it will collect; the image will therefore be brighter, or, amounting to the same thing, it will reveal fainter objects. In astronomy, where we are dealing with such dim things as stars, this consideration is a very important one.

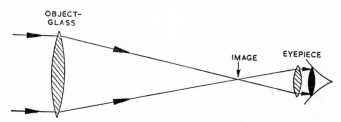

Fig. 1. *A refracting telescope*

The magnification of such a telescope can be found by dividing the distance between the object-glass and the image (the 'focal length' of the object-glass) by the distance from the image to the eyepiece (the focal length of the eyepiece).

Both object-glass and eyepiece are shown in their simplest form. In any telescope worthy of the name they consist of two or more lenses close together, the combination producing a better-quality image than a single lens.

A disadvantage of the telescope shown in Fig. 1 is that it gives an inverted view. Terrestrial telescopes always have additional lenses inside the tube to erect the image, but for astronomical work these are left out; the erector tends to distort the image, and it absorbs a slight amount of light—negligible for normal practice, but possibly of vital importance when trying to glimpse an excessively faint star. Inversion does not matter at all; drawings of the Moon and planets always show south at the top and east at the right, and one sure way of baffling a regular lunar observer is to show him a picture of the Moon the right way up!

For low-power work, however, it is certainly an advantage to have the orientation correct, since telescopic and naked-eye views can be easily compared. In any case binoculars have a

17　　　　　　　　　　　　　　**B**

system of prisms which effectively fold up a long telescope into a much more compact system, at the same time erecting the image.

Most people think that for any instrument to be at all usable for astronomical work, it must have tremendous magnification. This is a natural enough impression, and it is true that for certain studies (the remoter planets, for instance, or measurements of close double stars) a high power must be used. But no matter what the telescope, a high magnification has two attendant disadvantages. First, the image is made dimmer, because the same amount of light is spread over a larger apparent area, and second, the field of view of the telescope is decreased. It is precisely because they give a bright image and a wide field of view that binoculars are so useful.

Magnification is unimportant; the vital factor is aperture. There is no limit on this, provided the object-glass is of good quality. For example, a 2-inch lens will receive four times as much light as a 1-inch; in addition, fainter stars are more numerous, so that the larger instrument will outstrip the smaller by about six to one. Working it out on a star-density/cost basis, it is clearly the better investment!

Binoculars are always labelled X × Y, X being the linear magnification (e.g. the number of times longer a brick looks when compared with the naked-eye view) and Y the diameter of each object-glass, in millimetres. The usual conditions are 8 × 30, with a field of view of about 7°, so that fourteen Full Moons would stretch across a diameter. However, they can be obtained to 10 × 50 specification; the field of view is only slightly less, while the 50-mm. object-glasses collect nearly three times as much light. These so-called 'night glasses' are obviously far preferable for astronomical work.

Generally speaking it is not worth buying the very powerful 20 × 60 type; in any case, for the same price one could buy the ingredients for a good reflecting telescope. They are useful for looking at the Moon or for close double stars, but their high magnification means a prohibitively small field of view.

A good place at which to get a pair of binoculars cheaply is an ex-Government store, and these also supply those excellent instruments known as 'elbow telescopes', which are like the normal telescope except for having the eyepiece at right angles to the main tube. There is therefore no agonizing neck-strain when looking at something overhead, while for all other altitudes it is like peering down into a microscope. Elbow telescopes have recently come into their own for artificial satellite work; a typical example has a magnification of 8 diameters, an aperture of 2 inches (equivalent to 8 × 50 binoculars), and a field view of 6°. It costs only £3. In addition, they are much easier to mount on a stand than binoculars.

Some sort of mounting is absolutely essential; it is hopeless trying to observe if the instrument is not really steady. Slight shaking is imperceptible when looking at terrestrial objects, but stars are more exacting. A really solid camera tripod is a good solution, if it has a ball-and-socket or (preferably) a pan-and-tilt head. Once again an ex-Government supplier can probably oblige.

The old-fashioned opera glass is hardly ever seen today, but if a pair happen to be lying around they are certainly worth keeping. Their magnification is low (× 2 or × 3), and this combines with a large aperture to give a very bright view of the sky. For observing anything really diffuse and faint it may be the ideal instrument, and it has the additional advantage of needing no mounting.

Every astronomer, whether he uses binoculars or a 30-inch telescope, needs a star atlas. There is only one widely available, but luckily it is the best: *Norton's Star Atlas*, published by Gall & Inglis. It divides the sky up into 16 separate charts, shows every star visible with the naked eye, and includes notes on interesting objects. *Norton's* is used so widely that it is more or less a passport to astronomical circles.

Another semi-essential is the *Handbook* of the British Astronomical Association. The cost to non-members is 9*s*. (members get it free) and it contains details of eclipses, occulations, planetary movements and a mass of other data for the year in question. The B.A.A. also issues occasional Circulars to its members, giving details of new comet discoveries and other up-to-date news, and these are also well worth having. Altogether it is a good investment at the outset to join the B.A.A.

Just occasionally some interesting object, usually a comet, passes through the dawn or sunset region of the sky, and it is difficult to decide whether or not it will be visible against a reasonably dark sky. The answer here is a planisphere, a very simple device which can be set to show the sky for every hour of every day of the year. This is much better than trying to muddle around with one of the monthly newspaper star-maps, which do more than anything else to convince people that astronomy is an unintelligible science.

Finally, a word or two about the practical side of observing. Depending on circumstances, it takes the eyes at least ten minutes to get fully dark-adapted after going into the garden out of a lighted room; in the brightness the iris is shut down to about a tenth of an inch, and it is slow to expand to its most sensitive state. For this reason, keep any illumination needed for the map or a notebook to an absolute minimum.

It is interesting, and may be instructive, to compare the two eyes for sensitivity. With binoculars this is not very important, but with an ordinary telescope the situation is different. I have found that my left eye is appreciably more sensitive than my right, and often glimpses otherwise invisible stars. The eyes also see colours slightly differently, which seems to be a common phenomenon.

Always keep a notebook—right from the beginning, even when the observations seem to be of little value. Early drawings and notes will soon be of absorbing interest, and it is an old adage that an observer can always be judged from his records.

CHAPTER 2

The Sun

The coming of daylight gives no excuse for ending observation. In professional astronomy the Sun occupies a colossal department, for obvious reasons: it is our nearest star, and the only one we can study in detail. While binoculars cannot probe its secrets, they can at least provide an interesting commentary on the antics of its spots.

By our standards the Sun, the centre of the solar system, is huge. Yet its 864,000 miles of diameter is not too impressive on the stellar scale; if we turn to Betelgeuse, the red brilliant in Orion, its diameter turns out to be larger than the orbit of Mars. But we can hardly speak of its true diameter, for its surface cannot be properly defined; the gases simply become less and less dense, and like the upper reaches of the Earth's atmosphere eventually fade away into nothing.

The Sun, being smaller and therefore denser (for nearly all stars, regardless of their size, have approximately the same amount of matter in them), has a much more sharply-defined surface. We can see this surface, the 'photosphere', with the naked eye, and it marks the boundary of the solid, glowing solar matter. In actual fact, however, the Sun's average density is nothing like as great as the Earth's; it is composed mainly of hydrogen, and even though the pressure below the surface is colossal, it is not much more massive than the same volume of water.

The Sun

Sunspots

The Sun spins like an enormous planet, and we can time its rotation by watching the movement of sunspots—it works out to about $25\frac{1}{2}$ days, though due to the Earth's progress round its orbit it appears to take $27\frac{1}{4}$ days for a sunspot to return to the same place.

Strangely enough, we still do not really know how sunspots are formed. They are vast, relatively cool areas (the temperature of the rest of the surface is about 6,000° C.); they are strongly magnetic; and they have a powerful effect on terrestrial auroræ. These are caused by electrically unbalanced particles emitted by the Sun affecting the rarefied gas molecules in the upper atmosphere, and whenever a striking aurora is visible there are bound to be sunspots near the Sun's meridian.

Sunspots are certainly within the range of binoculars, though because of the fierce brightness and heat careful precautions must be taken in solar observation. There are two methods: projection of the image on to a screen, and direct observation through a dense filter.

Solar projection

Projection consists simply of holding a white screen a foot or so behind the eyepiece, and focusing the Sun's image on to it; to do this the eyepiece must be racked out considerably beyond the normal position. One of the object-glasses must, of course, be covered, and the viewing screen must be shielded from the direct solar rays to prevent hopeless fogging of the image.

While projection is an excellent method when used in conjunction with telescopes of moderate size, when direct viewing is always dangerous, the average binoculars are too low-powered to give a satisfactory image. Certainly it will not reveal nearly so many small features, and it is therefore not to be recommended.

Filter observation

In order to give protection from the tremendous radiation,

telescope makers usually provide darkened 'Sun-caps' which fit over the eyepiece; a typical Sun-cap consists of a small disk of thick glass, usually dyed a very intense green, inside a brass cell. They have two snags: one annoying, the other possibly lethal.

First, the glass separates the eye from the eyepiece itself and restricts the field of view. Second, although transmitting relatively little heat, they absorb a great deal. If placed at the focus of a powerful telescope the glass may expand irregularly and shatter from the stress. There is also the incidental difficulty of getting two identical caps.

All this comes about because the cap is at the wrong end of the telescope; its proper place is in front of the object-glass, so that it cuts out the harmful rays before they enter the instrument. With large apertures the cost of the filter, which must be of good optical quality, is prohibitive. Luckily binoculars are much more tolerant; I have found that two disks of densely fogged negative film, mounted in front of the lenses, will darken the image perfectly safely. Even better is the unexposed leader from certain types of colour film, which is a very dense green. The disks can be mounted inside two cardboard caps, which can be slipped on and off at will. Even if not perfectly flat, the film is so thin that it will have hardly any effect at all on the definition.

Observing sunspots

Binoculars will show a surprising amount of detail in the spots, especially if any of the groups happens to be complex. There are three broad divisions: unipolar, bipolar, and multipolar, depending on whether there are one, two or more main nuclei. The nucleus of a sunspot is its dark centre, or 'umbra'; surrounding this is a less intense annulus, the 'penumbra'.

Sunspots come and go, and their lifetimes can be measured in anything from just a few hours, for a tiny transient spot or 'pore', to several months. It is interesting to watch a group disappear at the western limb, and to wait for a fortnight to see if it survives the rotation and reappears at the eastern edge. Sometimes considerable groups grow very rapidly, in a matter of a day or two, and these sudden developments are worth watching out for.

Spot sizes are equally diverse. Some are so large as to be visible with the naked eye, when the Sun itself is suitably dimmed, either by an artificial filter or thick haze. Naked-eye spots must be at least 15,000 miles across (this includes the outlying penumbra), but some far larger ones have been observed. The greatest spot group ever known occurred on 7 April 1947; it was bipolar, with an overall length of nearly two million miles and an area of 6,000 million square miles, or twenty times that of the Earth!

Sunspot frequency fluctuates in an average period of slightly over eleven years. As yet we have no definite explanation of the sunspot cycle, and neither do we know why it is not completely regular; periods range from 9 to 13 years. The last maximum occurred when predicted, in the winter of 1957–8, and in December 1957 the Sun showed the most spotted disk ever recorded.

The drop after maximum is much slower than the build-up after minimum; weakest activity is expected in 1964, when binoculars may not show any considerable spot for weeks on end—on the other hand unusual things sometimes happen, a quite considerable group coming into view for no apparent reason, and a close watch should be kept on the eastern limb for any unexpected visitors.

Binoculars will also demonstrate a strange phenomenon known as Spörer's Law. At the beginning of a new cycle spots appear mainly in relatively high latitudes (about 30°), descending towards the equator as the cycle progresses, until after maximum they are mostly grouped in the two 10° latitudes. Around minimum, in fact, we usually have two spotted zones: low-latitude groups from the dying cycle, and high-latitude spots heralding the arrival of the next one.

Strangely enough, spots hardly ever appear very near the equator, and never near the poles; the most arctic spot ever recorded was in latitude 65°.

Accuracy in making daily drawings will come with practice, but there should certainly be no difficulty in detecting the solar rotation from day to day. Keep a special eye on the tiny spots near the limit of visibility, for these are breaking-out grounds for future groups—and remember that a great deal can happen to a region while it is on the averted hemisphere!

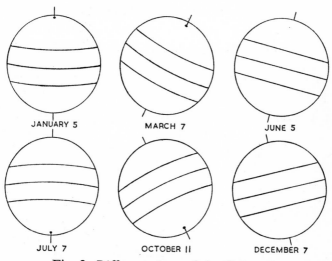

Fig. 2. *Different views of the Sun's axis*

On January 5 and July 7 the solar axis appears vertical (i.e. north and south). On March 7 and October 11 the north and south poles respectively are at their maximum presentation. On June 5 and December 7 the Earth passes through the plane of the solar equator.

The drawing gives the erect view, with north at the top. The Sun spins from left to right.

Careful observation over a number of months will show that the sunspots' apparent motion changes (Fig. 2). This is because the Earth's orbit lies at an angle with the solar equator. Starting off in June, when we lie exactly in its axis of rotation, they seem to move in straight lines from left to right. After that we drift slightly north, and the south pole disappears; the paths therefore appear curved. The maximum effect is in September, after which they straighten; in December the south pole reappears and the north moves off the disk, when the paths curve in the opposite direction.

For the same reason the solar axis appears to swing first one way and then the other. In July and January it is vertical. The greatest western tilt of the north pole ($26\frac{1}{2}°$) is on 8 April; the corresponding eastern tilt, on 11 October. Due allowance must be made for this when drawing in a north-south meridian line on the disk, though with binoculars the slant can be estimated only roughly. In any case the tilt from the vertical is true only at noon, when the Sun is due south; when rising its axis slants over to the left, and when setting it leans to the right.

Sunspots appear black, but this is simply due to contrast with the brilliant photosphere; they are really hot and glowing, though much cooler than the rest of the surface, and if they could be seen by themselves they would shine brightly. This is best seen during a solar eclipse, when they appear distinctly brown compared with the black lunar disk.

Solar eclipses

A solar eclipse occurs when the Moon passes in front of the Sun. This can obviously only occur at New, when the two are more or less in line anyway; if the Moon happens to pass exactly through the plane of the Earth's orbit, it will either partly or totally block out the brilliant solar disk.

Fortunately for us, the Moon appears about the same size as the Sun—the Sun is 400 times bigger, but it is also 400 times as far away—which means that at a central eclipse it is usually completely covered. Not always, however; the lunar orbit is not perfectly circular, and just occasionally an eclipse occurs when its distance has shrunk it too small. In this case the Sun's boundary appears as a complete ring, and the eclipse is called 'annular'.

Because the Moon only just covers the Sun, the region of totality on the Earth's surface for any particular eclipse is very restricted; the shadow is about a hundred miles wide, stretching eastwards as the Moon's orbital motion sweeps it over the surface. This means that the chance of any particular place witnessing a total eclipse is about once in three centuries, London being particularly badly off; its last eclipse was in 1714, while the next is not due until 2151!

The partial zone, of course, is far wider, and England usually gets one eclipse every two or three years; though at the moment things are rather barren, the next one not being due until 1966. After that six eclipses are visible before 1975:

TABLE I

Forthcoming Solar Eclipses

DATE			TIME			MAXIMUM PHASE
1966 May 20	.	.	9^h U.T. .	.		55%
1968 September 22	.	.	10^h	.	.	40
1971 February 25	.	.	9^h	.	.	60
1972 July 10	.	.	(sunset)	.	.	55
1973 December 24	.	.	(sunset)	.	.	10
1975 May 11	.	.	6^h	.	.	55

For obvious reasons the summer eclipses are likely to be seen under better conditions.

Binoculars can provide interesting views of partial eclipses. First of all there is the noting of 'first contact', which is the instant at which the Moon's eastern limb begins to cover the Sun; a publication such as the B.A.A. *Handbook* gives the time, and also the 'position angle'. Position angle is reckoned in degrees, starting from north (12 o'clock), round by east (90°, 9 o'clock), south (180°, 6 o'clock), and west (270°, 3 o'clock) (Fig. 3). Since the Moon first touches the Sun on its western limb, the P.A. of first contact is somewhere around 270°. The ever-widening segment should be visible after a minute or two. Keep a look-out for any sunspots that may be occulted by the lunar disk.

The duration of a partial eclipse, from first to fourth or last contact (the time at which the Moon moves completely off the

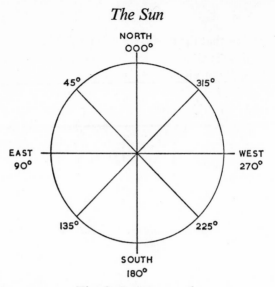

Fig. 3. *Position angle*

Sun) depends on its phase. It lasted about two hours on 15 February, 1961, when 93% was covered in London (though in actual fact the eclipse was total—cloud!), but when the phase is small the interval between contacts is naturally much shorter.

When a total eclipse occurs there are two more contacts, the second and third, at the beginning and end of totality. With minor exceptions, these few vital minutes are the only chance we have of seeing the solar atmosphere, or 'corona', in its own right; it glows like a pearly veil in the darkened sky. In ordinary daylight the corona is completely swamped by the Sun's glare, and professional astronomers may journey thousands of miles to observe a favourable eclipse. It is significant that the longest ones (they can never last longer than about 7 minutes 20 seconds, and are usually much shorter) always seem to occur in virtually inaccessible regions.

Other solar phenomena

When the Sun is very near the horizon our atmosphere plays strange tricks with its shape. The reason here is irregular refraction of light. When very low in the sky a star appears to be slightly higher than it really is; at an altitude of 10° the effect is about $\frac{1}{10}$°, but it increases to $\frac{1}{2}$° at the horizon. This means that a star or planet can actually be visible above the horizon after it has set, or before it rises. The Sun and Moon are both $\frac{1}{2}$° across, so that when they appear to rest on the horizon they are really below it.

The Sun's lower limb being more affected than the upper one, the effect of refraction is to squash the disk into a steadily more eccentric ellipse. Sometimes, however, remarkable distortions occur; the limb may become serrated, and on occasions the upper part of the disk appears separated from the lower. This happens when there are markedly divided heat layers in the atmosphere, since the degree of refraction depends on the temperature of the air the light is passing through.

Anyone who is fortunate enough to have a very low, preferably sea, horizon, can look out for a fleeting phenomenon known as the 'green flash'. It usually occurs just as the last fragment of the solar disk lingers on the horizon, when for the fraction of a second the colour changes from yellow to a bluish green. Apart from waiting for a very clear sky, which is essential, the main secret is not to look at the Sun until the last moment; from the point of view of avoiding dazzling the eyes, conditions are rather more favourable at sunrise provided the exact point of appearance is known beforehand. The flash itself is caused by a combination of refraction and absorption in the atmosphere. I have seen it only once, with the naked eye, but presumably binoculars will show it more easily.

CHAPTER 3

The Moon

Strangely enough, our nearest neighbour is slightly frustrating to the binoculars observer. It is near enough to be tantalizing, but not sufficiently close to show interesting detail without a fairly high power. It is here that the relatively powerful 15 × 40 or 20 × 60 binoculars come into their own, for the Moon has plenty of light to spare and the smaller field is, of course, no disadvantage at all.

Our one natural satellite has been in the publicity spotlight for some time now, and the basic facts are well-known. It is a much smaller world than the Earth, with a diameter of only 2,160 miles. In addition it is much less dense (it can have only a very small metallic core), so that its mass is less than $\frac{1}{80}$. The surface gravity is therefore considerably less, which means that it has been unable to hold on to any appreciable atmosphere at all.

The Moon revolves around the Earth at an average distance of 238,000 miles. This actually varies from 226,000 miles at its closest point, or 'perigee', to 252,000 miles at 'apogee', since its orbit, in keeping with all orbits in the solar system, is not perfectly circular. The difference is, however, so slight that for most purposes we can neglect its eccentricity.

The Moon's phases

Fig. 4 explains the lunar phases. At position A the Moon is very close to the Sun in the sky, and the night side is turned towards us; it is therefore invisible. This is New Moon. Gradually

30

it moves towards B, appearing first as a crescent in the evening sky and finally as a perfect half—this is First Quarter, which means that it has achieved one-quarter of its total journey round the Earth. Each quarter takes about a week.

As the 'terminator' (the line separating day from night) becomes convex instead of concave, we enter the gibbous phase. All this time the Moon is setting later and later after the Sun,

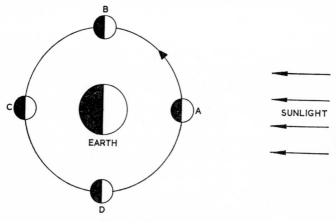

Fig. 4. *The lunar phases*

since it is getting farther away; by the time it reaches C the entire daylight hemisphere is turned towards us, it appears as a perfect circle, and it is opposite the Sun in the sky. This is Full Moon, when it rises at sunset and sets at sunrise. If the line-up is absolutely perfect there will be an eclipse, but we shall see presently that these are comparatively rare.

After Full the terminator passes to the opposite, or western, side. The phase begins to shrink, and the Moon rises late in the night when Last Quarter (D) is reached. After that it is visible as a crescent shortly before dawn, and after $29\frac{1}{2}$ days it is back at New again. This period is the lunar month.

Oddly enough, the Moon takes only $27\frac{1}{3}$ days to make one revolution around the Earth when measured relative to some stationary object, such as a star. This is because the phases depend on the position of the Sun. The Earth, as it moves along its orbit, carries the Moon with it; the direction of the sunlight is changing all the time, and to make up for this the Moon has to describe slightly more than a true revolution.

The surface features

Plates I to IV show the Moon at various phases. Notice, in particular, how the craters and mountain chains stand out along the terminator, where the Sun is still low in the lunar sky. Every feature casts its own private shadow, which has disappeared by local midday; the region then appears as a featureless, glaring mass of light. Observation of any particular feature is therefore most spectacular when it is seen during local morning or evening.

A glance at the Earth from a point out in space would reveal two striking divisions of the surface: the land and the sea. We can divide the Moon into the same two regions, though perhaps less accurately; the great dark areas, which are relatively smooth, are the seas or 'maria' (actually consisting of solidified lava, probably overlaid with dust), and the glittering rugged uplands are the land proper.

The craters which honeycomb the uplands are the characteristic lunar features. Basically they are huge saucer-like depressions, with rugged walls and frequently a colossal mountain group at the centre. Binoculars will show hundreds, especially in the southern hemisphere, and some are so big that smaller editions of themselves may be glimpsed on their floors. The 150-mile Clavius (see the outline map), near the south pole, is a good example.

When the newly-discovered telescope came into general use, astronomers spent years puzzling over the problem of crater-naming. Eventually the solution was found by an Italian priest named Riccioli, who published a map in 1651 on which he had called them after famous scientists and philosophers in general; it was a good idea because it served to keep their names constantly in mind, and also, as new craters came to light, so new names were available with which to decorate them. Nowadays they range from the ancient Greeks to contemporary astronomers, amateur as well as professional.

I. THE MOON, 4 days old. The larger craters shown in this and the following photographs are easily detectable with binoculars, and can be identified by means of the outline map. (Lick Observatory)

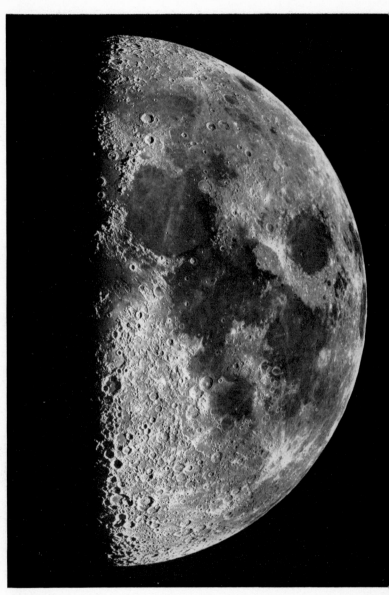

II. THE MOON, 7 days old. (Lick Observatory)

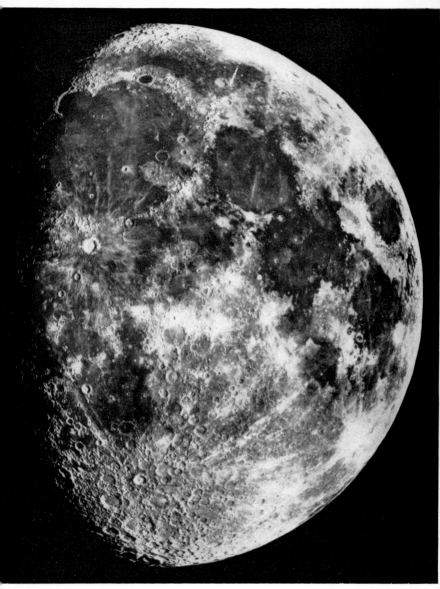

III. THE MOON, 10 days old. Compare the position of the Mare Crisium with that shown in Plate I. The two photographs were taken, respectively, near western and eastern libration. Note also the Sinus Iridum on the terminator. (Lick Observatory)

IV. THE MOON, 14 days old. The rays from the southern crater Tycho are now the most prominent feature. (Science Museum, London)

Due to the importance of having the terminator passing through the region under study, it is impossible to survey all the interesting features on just one night. With this in mind, the following remarks apply to the different phases from New to Full.

The thin crescent

When it first becomes visible in the evening sky one large feature dominates the crescent: the elliptical Mare Crisium, very near the western limb. Approximately 300 miles across, it is one of the smaller maria; nevertheless it is probably the most interesting of all. Binoculars will just reveal its mountainous border, and the best time to look at it is actually just after Full, under evening illumination. In a powerful telescope the apparently smooth surface of the mare is seen to be pimpled with tiny craterlets a couple of miles across, winding ridges running their way among them.

The Mare Crisium is a useful guide for revealing the lunar 'libration', or apparent slight swinging of the Earth-turned hemisphere from east to west and back again. The Moon's orbit is slightly elliptical, and from the universal laws of motion it follows that the closer a satellite is to its parent planet, the faster it must travel in its orbit. When the Moon is near perigee it therefore speeds up, and near apogee it slows down. Meanwhile, its axial rotation has remained steady. The result is that the two rotations periodically get out of step. At one observation the Mare Crisium may almost touch the limb, while twelve days later it will have swung well clear. This slow shift, once it is known to exist, can be easily detected with the naked eye.

Down south of the Mare Crisium is a prominent line of four craters: in order, Langrenus, Vendelinus, Petavius and Furnerius. They are all eighty to one hundred miles across. Vendelinus, on the shore of the Mare Fœcunditatis, has been broken down by the once molten lava—one of the many lunar Pompeiis to be seen all over the surface. The most interesting is Petavius, which has a fine central mountain and a deep valley running to

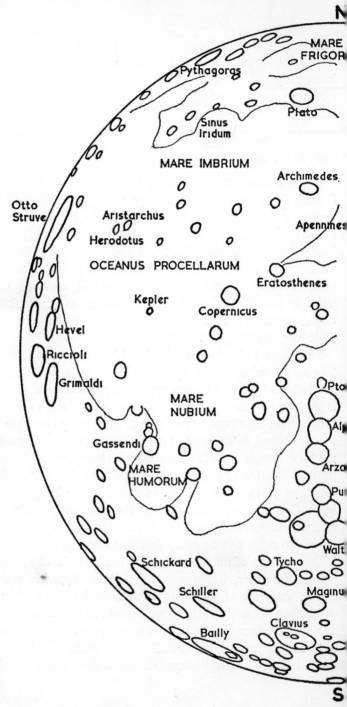

Fig. 5.

the south-east wall. Another conspicuous crater is Cleomedes, just north of the Mare Crisium.

The crescent Moon is highest in the spring, and when it is well-placed the dark side can nearly always be seen, glowing with a grey light; it is frequently very obvious with the naked eye, in which case binoculars will show some vague detail in the night hemisphere. The phenomenon, known as 'Earthshine', is caused by sunlight reflected from the Earth relieving the stark blackness of the lunar night. Our home planet must glow brilliantly in the star-studded sky, especially when there is a dense cloud cover, and Earthshine observations give some sort of clue to atmospheric conditions on our sunlit hemisphere.

Four days old

The terminator now passes through the Mare Tranquillitatis, and a fine chain of craters leads off its southern border: Theophilus, Cyrillus and Catharina. Less obvious crater-chains exist all over the Moon, and they give a clue as to the origin of these curious features.

There are, broadly, two main theories: the volcanic and the meteoric. The volcanic theory claims them to be purely geological features, the product of interior disturbances. The meteoric, attributes them to the impact of meteorites, citing as evidence several meteorite craters on the Earth (which would, however, be almost indistinguishable if placed on the Moon).

Crater-chains give positive evidence for the volcanic theory. In a slowly-solidifying crust, lines of weakness are bound to occur, and we should expect to find craters strung along them. The inference here is obvious, though it is only fair to point out that more technical wrangling has scored points for both sides.

In the southern hemisphere craters crowd the terminator and must be identified by means of the outline map. Of more interest is the group of three craters near the north pole: Atlas, Hercules and Endymion. In a large telescope both Atlas and Endymion are seen to have dark patches on their floors, and some observers consider them to vary in extent and tone during the lunar day.

Others oppose this view, and it is certainly hard to account for any such change.

First Quarter

Probably the most spectacular view of all is obtained when the Moon appears as a perfect half. The first thing to catch the eye is the great string of craters running down the central meridian. There are six main ones: Ptolemæus, Alphonsus and Arzachel; below them Purbach, Regiomontanus (a chart-confusing name) and Walter.

The 90-mile Ptolemæus is a magnificent object, and luckily for us it is almost exactly at the centre of the disk. In binoculars its floor seems featureless, but it really contains a great deal of fine detail; there is also a conspicuous craterlet Lyot (the eminent late French astronomer). Its mountain ring, however, is nowhere very high, and soon after the Sun has risen sufficiently high to douse the shadows its outline becomes very obscure. A neighbouring crater, Hipparchus, slightly smaller but once just as magnificent, has been so battered by the Moon's early geological upheavals that it is hardly recognizable at all except when close to the terminator.

In the northern hemisphere the Mare Serenitatis is well placed. Its south-west border merges with the Mare Tranquillitatis, while its eastern shore is defined by two magnificent mountain ranges, the Caucasus and Hæmus Mountains. Due north of the Caucasus are the Alps. These pay host to the curious Alpine Valley, which cuts so clean through the mountains that it looks as though some gigantic body just wiped the peaks out of its way. The 'grazing meteorite' theory can hardly be taken seriously, and like many lunar features it is a complete mystery.

Worth mentioning, even though it is invisible with binoculars, is the craterlet Linné in the Mare Serenitatis. Before the middle of last century it was seen and drawn as a distinct crater; now it appears as nothing more than a tiny pit at the centre of an extensive white area, and a comparison between appropriate maps shows a very marked contrast indeed.

Nevertheless, the Moon can play strange tricks. The look of a region changes amazingly from night to night as the sunlight strikes it from a steadily changing angle, and the Linné case could just possibly be put down to a remarkable coincidence of errors on the part of the earlier observers. At all events, it was the most concrete evidence of lunar activity until the Soviet astronomer N. Kozyrev detected gaseous carbon dioxide near the central peak of Alphonsus in 1959; this, at least, is quite definite.

Ten days old

It is a good idea to look at the Moon just after First Quarter, for this is the time when a magnificent mountain range can actually be seen with the naked eye. The mountains concerned are the Apennines, which sweep down across the central meridian. If the phase is just right their sunlit peaks jut out over the terminator, and for a few hours the little projection of light is easily visible.

The Apennines form the western border of what is probably the finest mare of all: the Mare Imbrium. It is now well in view; small craters are dotted here and there, but especially noticeable is the group of three in the shelter of the Apennines: Aristillus, Autolycus and Archimedes. It is somewhere in this vicinity that the Soviet probe Lunik II is reported to have landed.

Ranking with the most interesting craters on the entire Moon is the dark-floored Plato, on the northern shore. Regular in outline, its 60-mile floor is almost featureless in small telescopes. In larger instruments, however, a number of tiny craterlets appear, whose visibility seems to be strangely variable; it is just possible that occasional very slight hazes cover this and other regions on the lunar surface.

The finest crater of all, Copernicus, lies in the Mare Imbrium. It is a perfectly-formed crater, 55 miles across, with walls rising in places to 17,000 feet above the inner floor; in the centre is a superb mountain group, the central peak reaching to 22,000 feet. In a large telescope, when the lighting is just right, Copernicus is a wonderful object. It lies on a plain slightly elevated above the general level of the surrounding mare, and it is the centre of the second-largest ray system on the Moon.

Rays, the white streaks which radiate from certain craters like the spokes of a wheel, number among the many lunar mysteries. They are often hundreds of miles long, and the most prolific ray-centre, the 50-mile crater Tycho in the southern hemisphere, has given birth to a couple of streaks which extend for a thousand miles over the rugged, bleak landscape. Rays are best seen at midday (at Full they dominate the disk), and it is not at all certain what they are. They may be streamers of ash sprayed out from the central orifices of the craters concerned, but since it seems unlikely that the craters are volcanic in the terrestrial sense this explanation is nothing more than an unlikely guess.

Another lunar landmark is the beautiful Sinus Iridum, or Bay of Rainbows, on the northern shore of the Mare Imbrium. It is a semicircular cliff formation over a hundred miles across, looking very like the remains of a once noble crater that had its southern wall destroyed, and its floor flooded, by the relentless boiling lava of the young mare. When the phase is right the cliff juts over the terminator in a scimitar-like curve; a fine sight even in binoculars.

Somewhat south of Tycho is the most impressive crater of all: Clavius. It is 150 miles across and beaten into second place by the nearby Bailly, which has a diameter of 180 miles—but Bailly is a rather obscure object, close to the limb. Even binoculars will show a string of quite considerable craters spread across the floor of Clavius.

Full Moon

Near Full the brightest feature of all comes into view; this is the 23-mile crater Aristarchus, in the Oceanus Procellarum. All the uplands on the Moon are overlaid with a grey deposit, which presumably is volcanic ash, but the coating on Aristarchus is certainly unusual. It is one of the features which often show up distinctly under Earthshine conditions.

The Moon

Remarkable contrast is afforded by the nearby Grimaldi, a colossal crater 120 miles across, but so near the limb that we get only a very oblique view of its floor. This floor is of a dark steel-grey hue, even darker than that of Plato, and with the exception of one or two isolated spots it is the darkest surface on the Moon. Like the Mare Crisium, Grimaldi is a good guide for libration conditions.

Full Moon is, in general, the worst possible phase to observe; the sunlight is striking the surface from behind our backs, so to speak, and shadows are at a minimum. Just occasionally, however, Full occurs almost exactly in the straight line from the Earth to the Sun, and when this happens the sunlight is cut off for a time and we see a lunar eclipse.

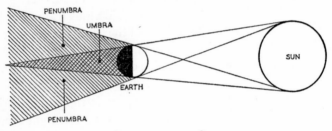

Fig. 6. *Lunar eclipses*

In the dark central cone, the umbra, all direct sunlight is cut off. This merges into the penumbra, where the Sun is progressively less and less obscured. In this region an observer on the Moon would see a partial solar eclipse.

Lunar eclipses

The Earth casts a tapering shadow in space, a shadow which at the Moon's mean distance is just over 5,700 miles wide. Moving at an average speed of nearly 2,300 miles an hour, our satellite can therefore remain totally eclipsed for up to 1 hour 40 minutes. Add to this the time taken for the phase to become total, as well as that spent in the lighter 'penumbra' of the Earth's shadow (as opposed to its darker core, the 'umbra': Fig. 6), and the total duration of a lunar eclipse can be over six hours.

The Moon

The Moon, however, never disappears completely when it passes into the umbra; the shadow is lit up by sunlight refracted inwards by our atmosphere. Red light is refracted most of all, which explains why the eclipsed Moon is usually a bronze or copper colour. We get red sunsets for the same reason.

This dependence on the atmosphere adds interest to eclipses; if the region through which the sunlight has to pass is unusually thick with cloud, the eclipse will be darker than average, while a transparent atmosphere will give a bright eclipse. Atmospheric conditions cannot be forecast with much accuracy, and there is always the chance of something unusual happening.

Twelve lunar eclipses will be visible in England before 1975; a list follows.

TABLE II

Forthcoming Lunar Eclipses

DATE			TIME			MAXIMUM PHASE
1963 July 6	.	.	22^h U.T.	.	.	70%
1964 June 24	.	.	24^h	.	.	Total
1964 December 19	.	.	1^h 30^m	.	.	Total
1965 June 14	.	.	1^h	.	.	20%
1968 April 13	.	.	4^h	.	.	Total
1970 August 17	.	.	3^h	.	.	50%
1971 February 10	.	.	19^h	.	.	Total
1971 August 6	.	.	20^h	.	.	Total
1973 December 10	.	.	1^h	.	.	10%
1974 June 4	.	.	22^h	.	.	70%
1974 November 29	.	.	(moonrise)	.	.	95%
1975 November 18	.	.	22^h	.	.	Total

Occultations

The Moon's orbital motion carries it once round the sky in its synodic period of 29½ days, which works out at an hourly velocity of about ½°—its own apparent diameter. This means that it must inevitably pass across and block out the stars in its path, a phenomenon known as an 'occultation'.

The Moon

Occultations of fairly bright stars are well worth watching, and can be seen just as well in binoculars as with a large telescope. First of all there is the slow approach of the Moon's limb; bright or dark, depending on the phase. Since it moves among the stars from west to east, disappearance will take place at the dark limb before Full and at the bright limb after. Reappearance, of course, is the reverse. Occultations occurring at the dark limb are especially spectacular, for the lunar disk is naturally invisible against the sky, and the star disappears or flashes out in the fraction of a second. This suddenness forms an incidental proof that the Moon's atmosphere is virtually non-existent, for a slight trace of air would produce a flickering and fading some time before the true disappearance.

The B.A.A. *Handbook* lists all favourable occultations, and a glance at the list will show that certain bright stars are fairly regular candidates. Regulus, in Leo, and Aldebaran, in Taurus, are frequently occulted, and when the Moon passes in front of an open star cluster such as the Hyades (which are associated with Aldebaran) several occultations may take place within a couple of hours.

When a planet is occulted, binoculars will show a few seconds' fading prior to complete immersion. This is because a planet, unlike a star, shows a perceptible disk, and it takes the Moon some time to cover it completely.

CHAPTER 4

The Planets

Most astronomical books are written in the wrong order, and this is no exception. If there is any excuse for starting off with the solar system and working up to the infinitely vaster stellar universe, it is that our nearby surroundings are of much greater personal importance. They are important because of their complete segregation from the rest of the universe, and to see how isolated our planetary system really is, the best way is to watch the course of a single beam of light after it leaves the Sun, travelling at its universal velocity of 186,000 miles per second.

After slightly over 3 minutes it passes Mercury; 6 minutes takes it to Venus; 8 minutes 20 seconds brings it to the Earth, with a $1\frac{1}{2}$-second jump to the Moon. Then comes a big gap; Jupiter, the first of the giant planets, is nearly three-quarters of an hour away, while outermost Pluto requires a journey of $5\frac{1}{2}$ hours before it is reached.

But after passing Pluto's orbit the light-beam can race on and on without the slightest chance of colliding with anything else —for 4 years and 4 months, the distance of the nearest star!

Put in its proper perspective, therefore, the solar system is a compact group. At its centre, vastly larger and more important than its family of planets, is our own private star: the Sun. Revolving round the Sun are the nine major planets, ranging from boiling Mercury to frozen Pluto, with the Earth third in distance.

The whirling Earth is our platform, and because of its position it automatically divides the solar system into two very unequal parts. Inside its orbit revolve the 'inferior planets' (Mercury and Venus), while the remainder, the 'superior planets' (Mars, Jupiter, Saturn, Uranus, Neptune and Pluto) lie outside.

The inferior planets

Because they are inside the Earth's orbit, Mercury and Venus can never stray very far from the Sun; Fig. 7 shows their movements. When at A an inferior planet is at 'eastern elongation', so called because it is then at its greatest angular distance from

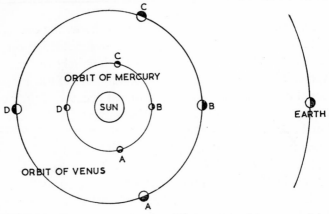

Fig. 7. *Movements of the inferior planets* (Not to scale)

the Sun, to the eastern side. Gradually its orbital motion moves it in to B, known as 'inferior conjunction'. At this position it is closest to the Earth, but it is too near the Sun to be observable; in any case the night side is turned towards us, like the Moon when New. It then moves out to C, which is western elongation, and finally it closes in towards the Sun again at D. At this position, 'superior conjunction', it is at its most distant. The times taken to complete these paths are approximately 116 days for Mercury, 584 days for Venus. These times take into account the Earth's own rotation around the Sun, and are the planets' synodic periods; a planet's true revolution period, or year (88 days for Mercury, 225 days for Venus) is called the sidereal period.

We see these orbits very inclined because all the planets move in almost the same plane; if we drew a plan of the solar system on a sheet of paper it would not be very far from the truth. Unfortunately, with the exception of Pluto (which seems to be exceptional in most ways) Mercury and Venus are the worst offenders. Mercury's orbit is tilted at an angle of 7° to our own, Venus's at $3\frac{1}{2}$°, and this has the unfortunate effect of making transits across the Sun at inferior conjunction rather rare; they usually pass either above or below the solar disk.

The best chance of seeing an inferior planet is obviously when it is at its greatest angular distance from the Sun, near either A or C. Western elongations must be seen before sunrise, while

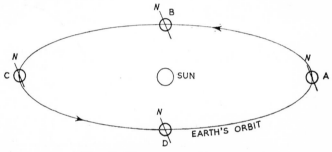

Fig. 8. *The seasons* (Not to scale)

This shows the Earth's orbit as seen from a point out in space somewhat north of the orbital plane. The Earth's axis remains fixed in direction.

at eastern elongation Mercury can set up to two hours after the Sun, and Venus, which moves in a larger orbit, can set four hours after and so be visible against a really dark sky. Not all elongations are, however, equally favourable—something which comes about through the $23\frac{1}{2}$° tilt of the Earth's axis (Fig. 8).

Position A shows the Earth at the time of northern mid-summer, when the north pole is turned its greatest extent to-wards the Sun—at this time it appears directly overhead at noon to someone in latitude $23\frac{1}{2}$°. Three months later it is at B, the vernal equinox (September 23), when the Sun is in the plane of the equator and appears to be travelling south. At C (northern midwinter) it is $23\frac{1}{2}$° south; after that it starts to drift north again and by March 21 (D) it is on the equator once more, travelling north. This, of course, is the explanation of the seasons.

This movement of the Sun can be represented as in Fig. 9, which is a panoramic view of the sky in the region of the celestial equator. The wavy line represents the Sun's apparent path north and south of the equator throughout the year, and it is known as the 'ecliptic'.

Since the Sun lies exactly in the plane of the Earth's orbit, the ecliptic is nothing more than the projection of our orbit in the sky. This is most easily understood by supposing the Sun to

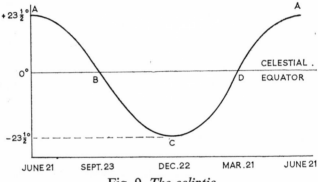

Fig. 9. *The ecliptic*

move round the Earth; it lies in the plane of our orbit, and wherever it moves it marks out that plane. Suppose for a moment that the Earth's axis were vertical. The equator and the ecliptic would then coincide, the Sun would always have the same altitude, and there would therefore be no seasons.

All the planetary orbits are in very nearly the same plane, and this means that their paths must follow the ecliptic very closely. Just as the Sun is highest (to a northern observer) when crossing the midsummer point on June 21, so is a planet. When it is near the midwinter part of the ecliptic it never rises high in the sky and so is difficult to observe adequately.

We can now return to the inferior planets, which present a special problem: the prime consideration here is their altitude above the horizon at sunset or sunrise. Fig. 10 shows two eastern elongations at sunset: one on March 21, the other on September 21. In both cases the angular distance from the Sun is the same, but the spring sunset is obviously far more favourable; the planet is in the north-bound part of the ecliptic, while in autumn it is in the south-bound region. Evening elongations are therefore best seen in the spring, and a little thought will

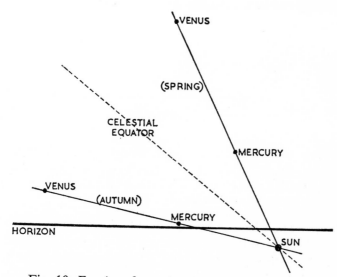

Fig. 10. *Evening elongations in spring and autumn*

Note that the planet's direction of setting is parallel to the celestial equator, not to the ecliptic.

show that the autumn is the best time to observe a western, or morning, apparition. These circumstances apply to both the inferior planets.

MERCURY

Mercury is a challenge for binoculars. Its greatest possible elongation from the Sun is only 28°, which must obviously occur when it is at aphelion, and because its orbit is very eccentric a perihelic elongation carries it only 18° away from the Sun

The Planets

(Fig. 11). By a piece of cynical planning on Nature's part the more favourable aphelic elongations always occur when the planet is well south of the equator, so that northern observers have to be content with far less spectacular views of the innermost planet. This is just one example of an occurrence which is so frequent in astronomy that it has been dignified with a name: Spode's Law. Spode's Law states quite simply that whenever something can be thoroughly awkward, it is.

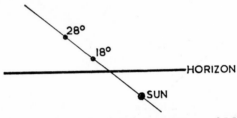

Fig. 11. *Perihelic and aphelic elongations of Mercury*

The difference between the two angular distances is exaggerated by the fact that the Sun must be some 10° below the horizon before the sky is sufficiently dark to allow Mercury to be seen.

Mercury may have to be chased, but it is not nearly as elusive as people make out; given a clear sky and a favourable position, binoculars will reveal it easily as a pinkish starlike object. The method is to plot the position on a map and obtain an approximate altitude at, say, an hour after sunset, when the sky will be sufficiently dark. It is no good trying to find it by reference to the stars, of course, since the sky will still be much too bright.

The B.A.A. *Handbook* gives positions for every fifth day during each elongation. Plot these in Norton's atlas, mark the position of the Sun, and then draw in the angle of the horizon (for latitude 52°, it is at an angle of 38° to the equator). Decide where the horizon line must be placed for the appropriate time after sunset, and the result will be amply accurate for wide-field binoculars. The lower the power the better, at least until the planet is located. Gauge the altitude above the horizon in terms of field-widths.

The Planets

TABLE III

Forthcoming Elongations of Mercury

There is little point in giving the precise angular elongation, since observing conditions depend so much on the season. However, all elongations greater than 25° are marked with an asterisk.

	ELONGATION EAST	ELONGATION WEST
1962	*September 10	October 22
1963	January 4	*February 13
	April 26	June 13
	*August 24	October 5
	December 18	
1964		January 26
	April 7	*May 24
	*August 5	September 18
	November 30	
1965		January 8
	March 21	*May 6
	*July 18	September 2
	November 13	December 21
1966	March 5	*April 18
	*June 30	August 16
	October 26	December 4
1967	February 16	*March 31
	June 12	July 30
	*October 9	November 17
1968	January 31	*March 13
	May 24	July 11
	*September 20	October 31
1969	January 13	*February 23
	May 5	June 23
	*September 3	October 14
	December 27	
1970		*February 5
	April 18	June 5
	*August 16	September 28
	December 10	

49

I remember following Mercury for five successive evenings in August 1955, using a pair of opera-glasses to locate it, noting its position with reference to some convenient chimneys, and picking it up with the naked eye. Just occasionally, when the atmosphere is exceptionally clear, it can become quite strikingly obvious.

Mercury occasionally passes close to a bright star. These so-called 'appulses' can be interesting, but they are usually difficult to observe; Mercury, shy as it is, is really much brighter than any of the stars it can approach. Appulses to Venus are more favourable, for Venus is bright enough to be seen under almost any conditions and can serve as a guide to the fainter planet.

Apart from the satisfaction of glimpsing it in the twilight sky, Mercury's main interest lies in its occasional transits across the Sun. The last was on 6 November, 1960, and it was easily visible with binoculars as a black speck moving slowly across the solar disk. Transits usually take about five hours, and the next two are those of 9 May, 1970, and 9 November, 1973.

VENUS

Venus is anything but modest. Every now and then the morning or evening sky contains a brilliant object that puts even the brightest stars to shame; when very near the horizon it shines like a distant lamp. It can sometimes be seen in broad daylight, and at a favourable elongation, when it glares down from a dark sky, it casts a distinct shadow.

There are several reasons why Venus is such a startlingly different proposition from Mercury. It is much larger—7,700 miles in diameter as against 3,100—and instead of being an airless, barren globe it is covered with dense cloud which reflects nearly 60% of the sunlight falling on it. Add to this its much wider elongations (they average 47°, hardly varying at all because the orbit is almost circular), and it is hardly surprising that Venus is the most brilliant planet in the sky. In addition its minimum distance from the Earth is a mere 26 million miles, as against 35 million in the case of the second-nearest neighbour, Mars.

To make the search for the Planet of Love worthwhile we have to manufacture difficulties. One is to look for it during the day; another is to catch it near superior or inferior conjunction. The best game is to follow it in towards inferior conjunction at the end of an evening elongation, to see how near the actual day of conjunction it can be spotted. With amateur-owned telescopes it has frequently been followed right through conjunction, when its distance from the Sun can never be more than a few degrees; at this time its phase makes it look like a very young Moon.

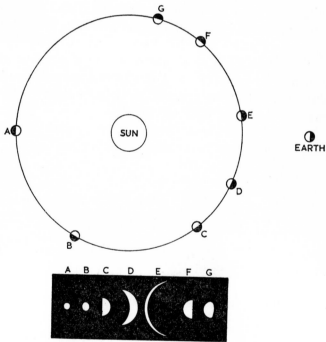

Fig. 12. *The phases of Venus* (Not to scale)

The phases of Venus

Fig. 12 explains the phases of Venus (or Mercury). In the first position, superior conjunction, its illuminated hemisphere

51

is turned fully towards us and it appears as a circular disk, shrunken by distance. Gradually its orbital motion sweeps it out east of the Sun and it comes into the evening sky, its phase lessening but its brightness increasing through its steady approach towards the Earth. At elongation it appears as a perfect half, and as it curves in towards inferior conjunction the disk quickly expands and the phase narrows into a crescent. At a certain point—when 28% of the disk is illuminated—maximum brilliancy occurs, distance and phase combining to the best advantage. When it reappears in the morning sky the phases are run through in the reverse order.

Good-quality binoculars should show the crescent phase quite easily, and the thing to remember is that magnification is not nearly so important as optical quality. This is so in all branches of astronomy, but Venus is an exceptionally severe test; its brilliance is so intense that it produces false glare in even a good telescope, and this glare masks the outline. If binoculars allow the crescent to be seen their excellence is certainly vindicated once and for all.

The B.A.A. *Handbook* gives all necessary position and phase data, and a table of future elongations is given below.

Table IV

Forthcoming Elongations of Venus

Once again visibility depends on the time of year. Elongations vary between $45\frac{1}{2}°$ and $47\frac{1}{2}°$.

ELONGATION EAST	ELONGATION WEST
1962 September 3	1963 January 23
1964 April 10	1964 August 29
1965 November 15	1966 April 6
1967 June 20	1967 November 9
1969 January 26	1969 June 17
1970 September 1	

The Planets

Daylight observation

When finding Venus during the day the easiest procedure is by timing its 'transit' or passage across the meridian. The meridian is the north–south line which passes directly overhead, and it is chosen because a celestial object reaches its highest altitude above the horizon when it is due south.

The Sun transits at approximately twelve noon, but the time varies up to 14 minutes either way at certain periods of the year; the discrepancy is known as the 'equation of time'. It comes about through the Earth's orbit being not quite circular. At perihelion (in January) it moves faster than when near aphelion (July), and even though the difference is relatively small it means that the Sun's apparent journey along the ecliptic is not at all regular. First it is ahead of schedule—later on it is behind, depending on where the Earth is in its orbit.

The first step is to look up the time of solar transit (making due allowance for that non-astronomical absurdity, Summer Time). The binoculars are then fixed on their stand and pointed towards the Sun at the appropriate moment, taking due care not to get an eyeful of the blinding disk. The position of Venus is then looked up and the difference between its and the solar R.A. noted (see page 95). This time is allowed to elapse, and after making due allowance for its different altitude the planet should be found without much difficulty.

Suppose that we observed the transit of 9 August, 1962. The Sun's position is in R.A. 9^h $15^m \cdot 5$; Dec. $+15° 55'$. Venus is in R.A. 12^h $01^m \cdot 0$; Dec. $-0° 11'$. Solar transit that day is at 12^h $05^m \cdot 5$ U.T.

After pointing the binoculars at the Sun at $5\frac{1}{2}$ minutes past noon (though a couple of minutes either way will make little difference), we wait for $2\frac{3}{4}$ hours. After this interval Venus is on the meridian. We then lower the binoculars through 16°, the difference of their declinations, and Venus should be in the middle of the field of view. The 16° can be judged by knowing the width of the field of view and using odd clouds as reference-points, but a better method is to fit a small protractor to the stand.

Of course anything can happen during the vital 2¾ hours, and Spode's Law is sure to come into play. It is also worth making sure that Venus itself will be accessible. I remember once using this method on a superb cloudless day, only to find that when I lowered the telescope after the requisite time interval it was looking point-blank at a chimney! The safest way is to check at once.

This procedure is obviously useless when Venus is a morning star and therefore leading the Sun across the sky. In this case find a way of marking the meridian, using some distant landmark, and work out the planet's altitude and time of transit.

Although we glibly speak of Venus being visible during the day with the naked eye, when near maximum brilliancy, it must be remembered that the slightest haze (permanent over most cities) can make it invisible even with a fair-sized telescope. Only when the sky is a rich blue is it accessible, and even then it requires certain practice to pick out the tiny speck of light. Once it is spotted it is obvious, but it may take some time to locate.

It is worth keeping this in mind when dealing with the occasional amazing claims for having seen Jupiter or Mars with the naked eye under daylight conditions. To achieve such feats requires perfect vision and an exceptionally pure sky, and only very rarely is the right observer in the right place at the right time.

Appulses to bright stars occur in the same way as with Mercury, but they are usually much more spectacular; when they happen in a bright sky Venus can be used as a guide to find the star. The best example of this was on 7 July, 1959, when Venus actually occulted Regulus not long after noon. Weather was generally good at the time, and the star could be seen with 3- and 4-inch telescopes once Venus was found.

Occultations of Venus by the young or old Moon are common, and since the planet shows a reasonable disk there is perceptible dimming over several seconds. Once again the best views are to be had from out-of-the-way stations like Rio de Janeiro, but just occasionally England plays host to one.

Transits of Venus across the Sun are very rare. They occur in pairs, the last being in 1874 and 1882, and the next are not due until 7 June, 2004, and 5 June, 2012.

The superior planets

A marked change comes over planetary movement when we shift outside our own orbit. Our gaze is not necessarily in the vicinity of the Sun, for it is obvious from Fig. 13 that a superior planet travels independently right round the ecliptic.

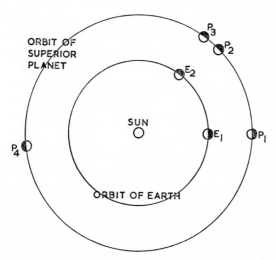

Fig. 13. *Movements of a superior planet*

The planet P, in the diagram, is closest to us at position P_1 when the Earth is at E_1—it is opposite the Sun in the sky, like the Full Moon, and the position is therefore known as 'opposition'. A little thought shows that at opposition a planet rises at sunset, is due south at midnight, and sets at sunrise; in other words, it is above the horizon all night.

Opposition passes and planet P moves along its orbit. But the Earth is also moving, and because it is closer to the Sun it travels faster. Thus, a year later it has returned to E_1, while the planet has only reached P_2. So all the Earth has to do is continue on its way for a little longer before it catches up with the planet and forms another opposition, at E_2 and P_3. The time between successive oppositions is the planet's synodic period. The intermediate position, P_4, when the planet is very near the Sun (and may be directly in line with it), is called 'conjunction'.

The more distant the planet the shorter is its synodic period. Suppose that there was a very remote planet whose yearly motion was negligible; then all the Earth would have to do would be to return to E_1 for another opposition. The planet's synodic period would be just one year, and it would never seem to move along the ecliptic.

Remote Pluto takes 248 years to circle once. This means that when the Earth has returned to the starting-point after an opposition it needs to go only about $\frac{1}{248}$ of a circuit further to catch Pluto up again—in other words, about $1\frac{1}{2}$ days. Jupiter, much closer to the Sun, has a sidereal period of about 12 years, so that oppositions take place $\frac{1}{12}$ of a year later each year, or at intervals of about 13 months.

Mars, the closest of the superior planets, is a rather more special case. Its sidereal period is just under two years, which means that by the time the Earth has returned to E_1 it has completed half an orbit, and is on the far side of the Sun, near conjunction. In this position, due to its greatly increased distance, it is unobservable, and in any case it is in too bright a sky to be visible. It takes another orbit and a couple of months before the three line up again, and Mars therefore has the longest synodic period of all: approximately 780 days.

At opposition a superior planet is opposite the Sun in the sky, so it follows that oppositions occurring when the Sun is in the lowest part of the ecliptic (i.e. during the winter) are the most favourable, so far as altitude is concerned. At a summer opposition a planet hugs the horizon and is badly placed for observation. Other considerations also apply to Mars, the first planet we meet on the journey beyond the Earth's orbit.

MARS

The orbit of Mars is noticeably eccentric (Fig. 14). Its mean distance from the Sun is 142 million miles, but this varies from 129 million at perihelion to 154 million at aphelion. Neglecting the variation in the Earth's distance from the Sun, opposition distances can therefore vary from 35 million miles (when it occurs with Mars at perihelion) to over 60 million at aphelion.

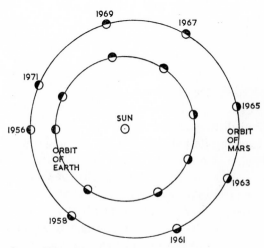

Fig. 14. *Oppositions of Mars*
The two orbits are drawn to scale.

The last perihelic opposition occurred in 1956, but since then the distances have been getting steadily greater. In 1958 the gap was 45 million miles; in 1961 it was about 56 million. Things will continue to deteriorate until 1965, but after that they will get progressively better until the next perihelic opposition in 1971. This variation means that opposition brightness varies; in 1956 Mars was a fiery ruby in the sky, outshining Jupiter for a time, and was quite unmistakable. But for the next few years it will only just outshine dull, leaden Saturn.

The Planets

From the point of view of northern observers perihelic oppositions are not necessarily the best. We saw earlier that Mercury
is more favourably placed for southern observers at its widest
elongations, and they also have the best of Mars; at perihelion it
is always well south of the equator. In 1956, for instance, it was
in celestial latitude $-10°$, which meant that from latitude $+52°$
it was only 28° above the horizon at its highest point (the equator
cuts the meridian at an altitude of 38°, since $90° - 52° = 38°$).
In 1958, on the other hand, its latitude was $+20°$, giving it a
maximum altitude of 58°. Atmospheric conditions are so much
better at a high altitude that northern observers had a better
view, despite the smaller disk.

Tracking the motion of Mars

Mars's disk is nearly always too small to look like anything
but a star in normal binoculars, though at a good opposition it
is just about distinguishable. However, they can do interesting
work in tracking its path among the stars (the word 'among',
of course, should not be taken too literally!).

Norton's atlas can be used as a basis for this work, but unfortunately it shows only naked-eye stars; and more comprehensive atlases are rather expensive. The best and most interesting
way out is to make a home-made chart. From the B.A.A.
Handbook mark out the region through which the planet will
pass during the next two or three months, chart the Norton's
stars on a large sheet of paper, multiplying the scale several
times, and fill in the fainter ones by observation. As well as
giving good practice in drawing star-fields, it is interesting to
later compare the chart with a more comprehensive map to get
an idea of its accuracy. Draw in lines of R.A. and Dec., so that
the observed and predicted positions of Mars can be compared.
Right ascension and declination, the longitude and latitude of
the celestial sphere, are explained on page 95.

The weekly motion of Mars along the ecliptic is obvious even
with the naked eye, and binoculars will show changes over a
much smaller interval. As the positions are plotted join them

into the most natural-looking curve that will fit, and date each entry.

Retrograde motion

If you follow a planet night after night, the textbooks say, you will eventually notice a most extraordinary piece of behaviour. Its normal easterly progress will slow down and slip into westerly back-tracking; after a time easterly motion will resume.

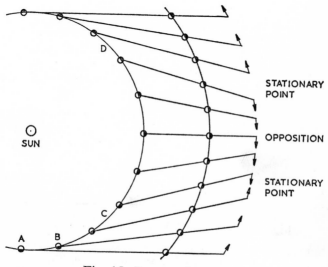

Fig. 15. *Retrograde motion*

The arrows indicate the apparent or proper motion of the planet.

The much easier way of discovering this 'retrograde' motion, by glancing at a planetary ephemeris, is less romantic but decidedly time-saving.

All the planets exhibit retrograde motion—even Mercury and Venus, which however camouflage it in the starless twilight sky. Fig. 15 explains it for a superior planet, when it occurs through the Earth's greater orbital velocity.

From our vantage-point we see the planet's motion projected

against the sky background—not the three-dimensional motion that it really is—and this apparent movement is called 'proper motion'. Starting with the Earth at A, we are looking at the planet more or less along the line of our own orbital travel, which means that it has no effect on the planet's proper motion; if we are heading directly towards an object it does not appear to shift relative to the background, though of course it expands in size.

By the time the Earth reaches B it is no longer travelling directly towards the planet, and its motion is having some effect;

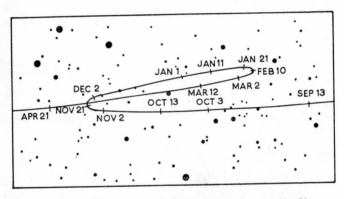

Fig. 16. *The path of Mars in the sky*, 1960–61

Most of the stars belong to Gemini; α (upper) and β are in the top left-hand corner, while XXX γ XXX is near the bottom. The area covered by the sketch is approximately 20° by 40°.

this effect is to slow down the planet's proper motion, since both the velocities are in the same general direction. Subsequently, as we approach opposition, the planet moves more and more slowly until the Earth reaches C, when the two velocities are effectively matched. After that the Earth's greater speed has the upper hand; it sweeps past the planet until D, when the velocities match again, and after that things proceed normally. The result is that the planet appears to backtrack for a time around opposition.

Retrograde motion was one of the chief headaches of Ptolemaic enthusiasts; an Earth-centred solar system could not account for it. It was eventually explained, together with other discrepancies, by supposing each planet to move in a small circle, the centre of which moved round the Earth in a larger circle. These 'epicycles' had a remarkably high birth-rate as more and more inaccuracies appeared; Ptolemy himself provided his system with over thirty, and later observers were forced to add more.

Fig. 16 shows the loop Mars performed in the sky during the opposition of 1960–61. Because of the angle at which their orbits are inclined, Mars, Jupiter and Pluto exhibit fairly open loops, while Saturn, Uranus and Neptune seem to retrograde along their own paths.

Mars poses its own problems, but these are strictly beyond the range of binoculars. So are its two satellites, neither of which is more than ten miles across; it takes a fair-sized telescope to reveal them at all.

Changes in brightness

The brightness of Mars changes very considerably throughout an apparition. The main factor is its changing distance from the Earth, but there is also its elliptical orbit to be taken into consideration; near perihelion it experiences markedly stronger illumination. There is also a slight phase effect when it makes the greatest angle between the Earth and the Sun, and telescopically it can sometimes appear like the Moon two or three days from Full.

When dealing with the average variable star (page 89) things are reasonably straightforward; it is simply compared with nearby stars whose brightness or 'magnitude' are known. Starfields do not change, and the same stars are always available for comparison.

But a planet, particularly a fast-moving and bright planet like Mars, presents two difficulties. First of all it wanders along the ecliptic, so that a star which is conveniently close in June may be nowhere to be seen by December. Another rather more serious objection is that the number of suitably bright stars is very limited; at its brightest Mars shines much more vividly than any star, and even at other times its marked orange colour makes comparison with normal white stars both difficult and uncertain. There are, in fact, only three stars of the right colour and brightness; they are α Boötis (Arcturus), mag. −0·06; α Tauri (Aldebaran), mag. 0·78; and α Scorpii (Antares), mag. 0·92. An explanation of magnitude classification is given on page 93.

These comparison stars will enable estimates to be made during the fainter stages of the apparition, but Mars far out-shines even Arcturus at the worst opposition.

The rotation of Mars

One claim which has frequently been made is that the rotation of Mars (its day is 24 hours 37½ minutes long) can be detected with nothing more vital than the naked eye—simply by its colour. The best analogy is the Earth itself. To an observer on Venus (supposing he could see anything through the clouds) the Earth's axial spin would present alternately the vast spread of the Pacific, then the main land-mass—two completely different hues; the change from the brown of the continents to the blue of the ocean would be obvious. But Mars, though similar in having most of its dark vegetation areas confined to one hemisphere, has much less contrast between these patches and the ochre desert.

The challenge is there, however, and it is certainly worth investigating by comparing its hue with nearby reddish stars. Binoculars are useless for this work which, like magnitude determination, requires a very large field of view; in any case, the brightness of Mars needs no augmenting.

It certainly needed no telescope to detect the unusual Martian conditions during the very favourable 1956 opposition. Instead of appearing pale orange its colour was almost yellow. Extensive dust-storms provided the cause; they obscured the surface features so effectively that things did not revert to normal until 1960.

A table of future Martian movements follows.

TABLE V

Forthcoming Oppositions of Mars

DATE	CONSTELLATION	MAG.
1963 February 4	. . Cnc . .	—1·0
1965 March 9	. . Leo . .	—0·9
1967 April 15	. . Vir . .	—1·3
1969 May 31	. . Sco-Oph . .	—2·0

THE MINOR PLANETS

On the first day of January, 1801, an Italian astronomer came across a starlike object that showed a planet's motion. This, the first minor planet to be discovered, was the result of much devoted searching, and fittingly enough is the largest. It is 430 miles across, named Ceres, and caused a stir in the astronomical world quite unmerited on the grounds of size alone; but it raised expectancy of many sisters, and even the most optimistic hopes have been over-fulfilled.

For Ceres was merely the prelude to the subsequent cascade of minor planet discoveries. Over two thousand have now been detected, most of which are hopelessly faint; but some of the brighter ones, which were naturally enough among the first to be discovered, are well within the range of binoculars. The B.A.A. *Handbook* normally lists four: Ceres, Juno, Pallas, and the brightest of all, Vesta, giving ten-day positions around the time of opposition.

The way to identify a minor planet is to draw all the stars in the field known to contain it. When the sketch is compared with the view three or four nights later, one of the 'stars' will have moved, betraying its planetary nature. Once it is identified, a minor planet can be followed until the evening twilight swallows it up.

Vesta can sometimes just be seen with the naked eye, but most of the time it is well below the threshold, and the others are permanently invisible. Even if no valuable work is possible, it is satisfying to watch one of these strange, barren worlds pursuing its lonely path across the sky.

JUPITER

The giant of the solar system never approaches closer than about 370 million miles (ten times the minimum distance of Mars), but its huge disk, 88,700 miles across, makes it appear much larger than the Red Planet. Binoculars easily reveal it to be something other than a star, and with a little perseverance they should show its four brightest satellites.

Jupiter circles the ecliptic much more slowly than Mars; it takes nearly twelve years to complete a circuit, and because of this there is less motion to track. The visibility chase, however, can be continued longer, and Fig. 17 explains why.

A planet is at its minimum distance at opposition, and maximum distance at conjunction; in the case of Mars the average distances are 48 million miles (M_1) and 234 million miles (M_2), meaning a fivefold change. Jupiter, however, is moving in a much larger orbit. Its mean solar distance is 483 million miles; at mean opposition it approaches to within 390 million miles (J_1), while at conjunction it recedes to 576 million miles (J_2)—only $1\frac{1}{2}$ times the opposition value. It is obvious that the more remote the planet, the closer the two values will match.

Planetary brightness follows the normal inverse-square law; at twice the distance a planet is four times as faint. It therefore follows that Mars at conjunction is only $\frac{1}{25}$ as bright as at opposition, while Jupiter loses only half its light. Bearing in mind the additional fact that Jupiter nearly always outshines Mars at opposition, it becomes obvious why the giant planet is much better prey for binoculars in the twilight evening sky as it moves in towards the Sun.

The satellites of Jupiter

The four bright satellites provide interesting entertainment. If they were removed from Jupiter's presence and scattered in the sky they would be visible with the naked eye; what makes their detection more difficult is the close proximity of the brilliant planet. The best time to look at them is when they are at their individual elongations.

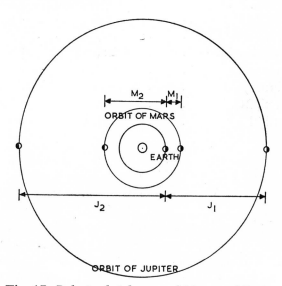

Fig. 17. *Relative brightness of Mars and Jupiter*
The orbits are drawn to scale.

The closest, Io, is naturally the most difficult; it is never more than three planet-diameters away. Europa is slightly more co-operative, but the third, Ganymede, is easy—it has frequently been seen with the naked eye. The outermost, Callisto, wanders up to 12′ away from Jupiter, but it is the faintest of the four.

These satellites, discovered by Galileo in 1610, are always

spread out in a straight line; they move exactly in the plane of Jupiter's equator, and since its pole is nearly vertical (as against our $23\frac{1}{2}°$ tilt) we always see their orbits edge-on. Jupiter's four moons, the brightest of twelve, provide one of the spectacles of the sky—a sight not denied good binoculars and the usual dose of patience.

TABLE VI

Forthcoming Oppositions of Jupiter

DATE	CONSTELLATION	MAG.
1963 October 8	Psc	−2·5
1964 November 13	Ari-Tau	−2·4
1965 December 18	Tau-Gem	−2·3
1967 January 20	Gem-Cnc	−2·2
1968 February 20	Leo	−2·1
1969 March 21	Vir	−2·0
1970 April 21	Vir-Lib	−2·0

SATURN

It is a sad piece of irony that Saturn, the most beautiful object in the entire sky, should be such a dead loss without a powerful telescope. It is sufficiently bright to be easily identifiable, so there is no interest there; its movement is too slow to be of continuous interest, and it has no bright satellites. To make matters worse it is well down in the southern doldrums at the present epoch, and with a synodic period of $29\frac{1}{2}$ years it is in no great hurry to crawl back up north again.

If they are of good quality, high-powered binoculars will show Saturn's elliptical outline quite distinctly (the general form of the planet was discovered by Galileo with a telescope magnifying only ×30, and its optical quality was very inferior by present-day standards). However, this whole matter raises a

Table VII

Forthcoming Oppositions of Saturn

Saturn's considerable range of brightness is due not to varying opposition distance but to the presentation of the ring system. When they appear at their widest (at an angle of 28°) they actually reflect more light than the planet itself; this happened last in 1958, and is due again in 1973, when Saturn will appear unusually brilliant. Conversely, when the Earth passes through the plane of the rings, as it will in 1966, the planet appears relatively dim.

DATE			CONSTELLATION			MAG.
1963 August 13	.	.	Cap	.	.	0·5
1964 August 24	.	.	Aqr	.	.	0·6
1965 September 6	.	.	Aqr	.	.	0·8
1966 September 19	.	.	Psc-Aqr	.	.	0·8
1967 October 2	.	.	Cet	.	.	0·6
1968 October 15	.	.	Psc	.	.	0·3
1969 October 28	.	.	Ari	.	.	0·1
1970 November 11	.	.	Ari	.	.	—0·1

question of fundamental importance which is certainly worth going into in a little more detail—the question of 'resolving power'.

The position can be illustrated as follows. Suppose we point a pair of 20 × 60 binoculars at Saturn and focus carefully; at its best, the image will appear as a tiny elliptical blob of light, with no detail visible at all. Now use the same magnifying power on a small astronomical telescope of 4 or 5 inches aperture. The image will naturally be the same size, but it will show far more detail; the ball of the planet can be distinguished from its ring system, and may show fragmentary markings. Not very well, of course, but the superiority of the view will be undeniable. It is due to the improved resolving power of the larger telescope.

This matter of resolving power is of great importance in astronomical work, and it explains why big telescopes can detect much finer lunar or planetary detail than smaller ones; the secret is not so much magnification as aperture. A 2-inch telescope, for instance, could not detect a lunar cleft less than 400 yards across, no matter what magnification was used, whereas a 9-inch telescope could show clefts down to 100 yards across. Resolving power is an inherent part of the optical system, and within certain limits it is unaffected by magnification.

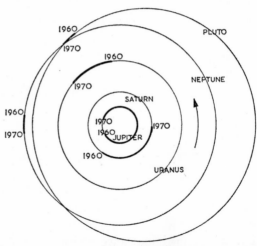

Fig. 18. *Movements of the superior planets, 1960–70*

The orbits are drawn to scale. Notice how the more distant planets not only move more slowly but also have a much greater distance to travel. Pluto is equidistant with Neptune from the Sun in 1969.

There is also the question of optical excellence. Despite what advertisements boast, binoculars rarely even approach the perfection of a good astronomical telescope. There is a simple reason for this: it is not necessary. They use a relatively low magnification and are normally confined to terrestrial viewing which is much more tolerant of slight imperfections than a bright star—the severest test any telescope can be given.

THE OUTER PLANETS

Uranus and Neptune, the brightest of the three newly-discovered members of the Sun's family, are not exactly ostentatious—but neither are they anything like so difficult to find as most people seem to believe. Uranus is in fact visible with the naked eye when its position is known, and its slow drifting round the zodiac (one circuit takes 84 years) can be followed from season to season just by casual observation. The periodic time of Neptune is 168 years; binoculars are needed to find it, and a few nights must be spent identifying it by its motion, but once it is recognized there is no danger of it slipping away among the stars. Even if no valuable work can be done, it is always satisfying to turn the binoculars on to their region (at the moment Leo and Libra respectively) just to make sure that a couple of our fellow-planets are still in their proper places.

Though considerably smaller than Jupiter and Saturn, Uranus and Neptune are still giant-sized compared with the Earth, with diameters of 29,300 miles and 27,700 miles. But distant, lonely Pluto is inferior to everything except Mercury; its remoteness, to the tune of 3,650 million miles, carries it beyond the reach of most amateur telescopes, and its orbital crawl makes it spend about twenty years in each constellation. At the moment it is in Leo.

All in all, there is very little work of value to be done on the planets. It is exciting to pick up the shy Mercury in the dawn or evening twilight, interesting to watch Mars change in brilliance as it swings near the Earth and performs its loop in the sky, and a test of patience to glimpse some of Jupiter's satellites. But luckily there are some more co-operative members of the solar system: comets and meteors.

CHAPTER 5

Comets, Meteors, Auroræ

Comets and meteors are the object of notorious confusion among non-astronomers. We frequently hear of someone having seen 'a comet dash across the sky last night', when they really mean a meteor; unless carefully watched, comets show no individual motion over an hour or two. There is indeed a relationship between the two, but it is a rather more subtle one.

COMETS

Comets are habitually referred to in hushed, awed voices, but in actual fact there is very little mystery about their movements and composition. They are composed of meteoric dust (hence the connection) and frozen gases, the main one being carbon dioxide. They move round the Sun like an ordinary planet, except that their orbits are nearly always very long, thin ellipses instead of almost perfect circles. The consequently great change of brilliancy in different parts of their orbits means that they can be well observed only when nearest the Sun—around the time of perihelion.

Comet-hunting

There is another difference also, for cometary orbits do not observe the solar system's general plane; whereas all the major planets except Pluto keep to within a few degrees of the ecliptic at all points along their paths, comets can wander all over the sky. So far as comet-hunting is concerned, their refusal to obey normal solar system regulations is both inconvenient and a blessing. It is awkward because a bright comet may appear anywhere in the sky, and encouraging because the large area to be searched makes it more likely that someone else has overlooked one.

Luckily there is one time-saver. A comet is brightest when near the Sun, both because of the increased sunlight and the tremendous increase of temperature, which excites the frozen gases and causes them to vaporize and glow. This is what produces the tail, the light-pressure actually forcing the glowing gases away from the Sun. It follows that the regions most likely to produce a fairly bright object are the late evening western sky, and the eastern sky just before dawn. Comet-hunters know this, of course, so they are naturally the most closely patrolled. But just occasionally amazingly bright specimens somehow manage to slip through the net and get caught only as they start to dim and sneak back into interplanetary space, so there is no need to be unduly pessimistic.

Success in comet-seeking depends 95% on the individual, 5% on the equipment, and an entirely unpredictable bonus for luck. The requirements for the observer are fairly obvious: indomitable patience and a rather phlegmatic outlook, as well as an almost intangible inner faith; rather formidable qualities which explain why comet-hunters are members of a lonely cult.

Equipment for comet-hunting

The instrument question, however, can be got to grips with more easily. The prime *desideratum* is large aperture, and all other factors being equal the larger it is the fainter the comet it will detect. The other important features, low magnification and wide field of view, are all embodied in binoculars. George Alcock, Britain's leading observer of comets, uses 5-inch binoculars magnifying ×25, and any type with object-glasses more than about two inches across can be of real service.

In a field of work such as this, where large aperture is really important, the best way of getting a serviceable instrument cheaply is to buy an ex-Government elbow telescope. There are several patterns available for a few pounds each, and they are all wonderful value—they have proved ideal for satellite tracking. Buy two similar models, mount them side by side, and they are the equivalent of a pair of binoculars worth four or five times the cost.

As in all other spheres of observation the binoculars must be really firmly mounted, for the slightest shake may obscure a faint stain on the sky background which could later grow into a magnificent comet.

When trying to glimpse an excessively faint object, whether it be a star, comet, or even a fine piece of lunar detail, it is well worth trying the dodge of 'averted vision'. In this technique the eye is directed to another part of the field of view while attention is concentrated on the object; this brings a more sensitive part of the retina into use. Another way of coaxing otherwise invisible objects into view is to slowly swing the binoculars from side to side; the movement amplifies the brightness. This is especially valuable in bringing out the faintest extremity of a comet's tail.

Sweeping for comets

Once the region is selected, it is covered by means of a large number of horizontal 'sweeps'. The glasses are very slowly swung across an arc, every suspicious object passing through the field of view being examined minutely; at the end of the arc they are raised or lowered and an overlapping sweep made in the opposite direction. It is a slow and tedious business, demanding great concentration, for the slightest lapse of attention might mean the loss of a long-awaited comet.

There must be some means of identifying any dubious objects, and it is here that difficulties arise. *Norton's* shows all the brighter nebulæ and clusters, some of which may look rather cometic with low powers, but it is not quite comprehensive enough. The answer, in the case of an unidentified object, is to watch it for an hour or two; if it is a comet, it will move. The mere absence of a tail is no evidence at all, for few comets develop any conspicuous appendage until they are very near perihelion. To avoid the humility of finding that a 'discovery' is simply an independent sighting of a known comet, subscribe to the B.A.A. Circulars.

Of course, amateur comet-seekers are in fierce combat with professional astronomers. Few observatories include it as a regular part of their programme, but every now and then a faint comet is picked up on a photographic plate exposed for some other purpose; while the wide-angle 'patrol' plates, which are intended to pick up anything new in the sky, have collected their share as well. With these other agencies at work, it is perhaps surprising that amateurs have done as well as they have.

Even so, comets do not simply turn up at the drop of a hat. Regular comet-seekers (and there have been only five or six during the past century), using adequate equipment, find that each of their comets requires roughly 300 hours of searching. And these 300 hours must be carefully salvaged. First offender is the weather, which makes at least 50% of nights unsuitable. Then there is moonlight, which between first and last quarter makes the sky prohibitively bright for much of the night. Domestic callings use up a fair percentage of the remaining time, so it is no wonder that the keenest enthusiast might take several years to muster his 300 hours. And there is no guarantee at all that a lifetime's work will produce the coveted comet. It requires intense devotion to duty and an overwhelming desire to succeed.

But there is one compensation. Every comet-seeker, whether or not he sees his name go into a comet catalogue, earns a superb working knowledge of the night sky. As the same region is slowly swept over night after night, gradually being displaced by the progressing seasons, every star unconsciously becomes a remembered landmark. The patterns of thousands of Milky Way brilliants are immediately recognized, and the telescopic clusters can be picked up almost without thought.

Part of the reason for the cult being a lonely one is the common inability to stay up late or rise long before the perkiest lark (it is useless to search once the sky is even tinged with day). There is also the irritating horizon difficulty; clear east and west views are very important for surveying that part of the sky near the Sun, and if these are not available it seriously reduces the chances of success.

Observing comets

In this case there is the less exciting but just as important business of following known comets. The B.A.A. *Handbook* gives details of expected returns, and the Circulars give more up-to-date news. It is in the observation of new comets that binoculars can do really useful work, for they are notoriously unpredictable.

Some examples may be given. The early behaviour of the first of the two bright comets of 1956, comet Arend-Roland, which reached perihelion at the end of April, suggested that it might become a really striking object. More recently, in 1959, Alcock's two comets failed to live up to expectation; especially the second, which disappeared completely after passing perihelion. Stories of more historic comets behaving as the mood took them are legion. They simply cannot be trusted, and binoculars can do really valuable work—especially if one is placed in a bright twilight sky which will fog a photographic plate.

Apart from physical change, their movements are often interesting. Concentrated attention will reveal a slight drift in a matter of minutes if the comet is fairly near the Earth, and this is the time to watch for passages in front of stars. These cannot be predicted with any certainty, so it is up to the observer to watch for occultations as they happen. Timing the closest approach of the nucleus (the bright, usually well-condensed portion) to the star may be of use if it is accurately done, and provided the star in question can be identified afterwards!

Comets, Meteors, Auroræ

METEORS

The connection between comets and meteors was demonstrated, strikingly, by the celebrated comet discovered by Biela in 1826. At the 1845 return it was observed to actually split into two distinct units—an unprecedented event. In 1852 (its period was about six years) the two components were still within earshot of each other, but at the next two returns nothing at all was seen. It should have returned again in 1872; instead, there was a magnificent meteor shower at the time when the comet should have passed close to the Earth. The inference is obvious: comets consist mainly of meteoric particles, and it is now known that many of the principal meteor showers are associated with the orbits of known comets.

A meteor, in its own right, is a tiny granule of matter no bigger than a grain of sand, circling the Sun in a normal orbit. If left to its own devices it would keep on eternally, but there is just the remote chance that it will pass too close to the Earth and be pulled down to the surface. When this happens—and millions of meteors are captured daily—it shoots through the atmosphere at such a velocity that it momentarily turns white-hot. This is the 'meteor' that we see with the eye.

Meteor showers

On almost any night of the year, provided the sky is really dark (and towns are no place for comet or meteor work), six or eight faint meteors will streak at random among the stars. These are called 'sporadic' meteors. But at certain times of the year, notably August and December, definite showers occur. Perhaps 'shower' is an over-ambitious word; it simply means that the meteors all appear to come from the same part of the sky, and they occur when the Earth passes through a swarm of meteoric particles.

This is where their relationship with comets comes in. As a comet pursues its path round the Sun a certain amount of its meteoric content gets left behind, so that there is a trail of debris circling perpetually in its orbit. If the Earth's orbit chances to cut the comet's path it will experience a sudden increase in meteoric activity. This produces a shower, and since the two orbits are fixed in space it must obviously occur at the same time every year.

Meteor shower densities can vary from about two to sixty naked-eye meteors per hour. If the trails belonging to a particular swarm are plotted on a star map and traced back, they will be found to radiate from a certain region of the sky: the 'radiant'. This is actually an effect of perspective; the meteors are travelling in parallel paths, but they are so far apart that their trails appear to widen as they approach.

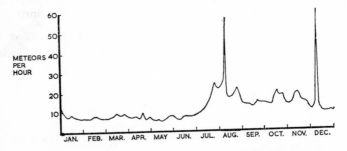

Fig. 19. *Meteor rates throughout the year*

The figures refer to real, not zenithal, hourly rates, as seen from England. Though actual results depend enormously on observing conditions (it is therefore perhaps misleading to quote specific rates) the graph does at least show that autumn is the best time of the year for casual meteor observation. The two main showers are the Perseids and the Geminids.

The constellation in which the radiant is situated gives the shower its name. The August meteors radiate from Perseus and are called the Perseids; Gemini provides the December shower, which are known as the Geminids. Sometimes the same constellation plays host to two or more showers at different times of the year, in which case the brightest star near the radiant provides the distinction. For example a shower on January 17 radiates from ϰ Cygni; the meteors are called the ϰ Cygnids to distinguish them from a shower which occurs round about the end of July. The radiant star in this case is α, and they are called the α Cygnids.

Observing meteor showers

Twenty years ago meteor observation was almost entirely in amateur hands, and the universal instrument was the naked eye. What observers did was to lie on their backs gazing up at the stars, noting the points of appearance and disappearance of each meteor and quickly plotting it on a chart. By this means a great deal of information could be obtained about the nature of the radiant (whether it was sharply defined or spread over a large area) and how it moved during the duration of the shower. Since the Earth is moving through the swarm all the time, it is to be expected that the meteors will appear to change direction slightly.

But times have changed, and professional astronomers have now entered the field armed with photography. This has become possible only very recently, with the advent of super-fast emulsions and wide-aperture cameras, but the advantages are obvious: the trails can be recorded far more accurately than by the best visual plotting, so that the derived results are more accurate. It does, however, suffer from one drawback. Photography can record only the brighter meteors, so that knowledge of the fainter members is still more or less in amateur hands.

With this in mind, the naked-eye observer has a simpler but also less spectacular job. All he has to do is count the meteors as they appear, noting the change of number that are recorded during fixed intervals throughout the shower. These intensities, when plotted on a graph, give an indication of the variation in strength of the shower and the epoch of maximum activity.

The Perseids, one of the most dependable showers, can be taken as an example. Maximum activity usually occurs early in the morning of August 12, so to cover the main period observations should, ideally, be continued from dusk on August 11 to dawn (like comet-seeking, meteor observation needs patience). Outliers of the Perseid swarm are first seen at the end of July and continue for a fortnight or so after maximum, but it is only the phase of greatest intensity that is of real interest.

It gets dark by about 21^h, when Perseus is low in the north-east, and attention is therefore concentrated on this part of the sky. A record is then kept of all Perseids seen in each complete hour: 21^h to 22^h, 22^h to 23^h, and so on—incidentally, never use Summer Time in recording observations; keep to Universal Time (U.T.) which reaches 24^h at midnight. During the first hour perhaps only ten meteors will be seen, but as the night wears on the intensity will increase. Reject any meteors which are obviously sporadic.

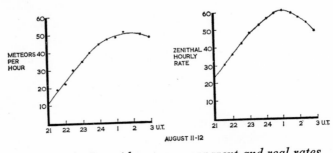

Fig. 20. *The Perseid meteors: apparent and real rates*

In practice, the Z.H.R. curve is never as neat as the one shown here!

When observation is over it is a good idea to plot a graph of hourly rate against time (Fig. 20). The result will probably be a steadily rising curve which drops down again late in the night, and from the graph in question it appears that maximum activity occurred at 1^h U.T. on August 12. These results are of course fictitious, and the curve is much neater than any actual curve is ever likely to be, but at least it illustrates the method.

Correcting the rate

In placing the time of maximum, however, an important factor has been forgotten. Perseus has been rising steadily throughout the night; it is still rising at dawn. This means, of course, that the altitude of the active area of the sky has also been increasing. At 21^h the radiant is only 27° above the horizon; at 23^h it is 37°; at 1^h it is 51°, and at 3^h, just before dawn, it is 66°. The inference is obvious; the increased altitude is going to mean firstly that a fair percentage of the early meteors occur below the horizon, and secondly that they have to be seen through a thicker layer of air, so that the fainter ones are drowned altogether. We know that stars appear dimmer near the horizon, and the same naturally applies to meteors. Hourly rate is therefore intimately connected with the radiant's altitude, and there must be some means of correcting for this. These means are embodied in the following table.

TABLE VIII

Correction for Zenithal Hourly Rate

This table gives the factor by which an observed hourly rate, with the radiant at a given altitude, must be multiplied to obtain the Z.H.R. It is a theoretical table only, applying to excellent sky conditions; moonlight or slight haze may easily double or treble the factor if the radiant is low, so it must not be treated too dogmatically.

ALTITUDE	FACTOR	ALTITUDE	FACTOR
2·6	10·0	34·5	1·6
8·6	5·0	42·5	1·4
14·5	3·3	52·2	1·25
20·7	2·5	65·8	1·1
27·4	2·0	90·0	1·0

These factors give the amount by which the observed rate for the appropriate altitude must be multiplied in order to obtain what is known as the Zenithal Hourly Rate. This is the rate always quoted in meteor shower predictions: it is the number of meteors that would be observed per hour were the radiant exactly in the zenith.

The hourly-rate graph can now be corrected. For example, we see that the rate at 27° is only half of the Z.H.R.; it is therefore doubled. When all the points are treated in this way the resultant curve looks (or should look!) like that in Fig. 20. Not only is the observed curve fictitious, but it places the time of maximum activity nearly an hour too late, the result of the radiant rising ever more favourably into the sky.

Meteor observation is one field of astronomical research in which co-operation of observers is almost essential, and the Meteor Section of the B.A.A. collects observations from amateurs all over Britain and combines them into a much more comprehensive result. No special requirements are needed apart from patience and, possibly, insomnia.

There are many recognized meteor showers, and they all have interesting peculiarities. A list of the main ones, together with details, is given in Table IX.

Apart from the weather, which always turns adverse on vital nights, meteor observation is severely handicapped by strong moonlight. A brilliant Full Moon will drown all but the brightest stars, and it is naturally futile to search for a faint shower under such conditions. Moonlit periods vary each year, affecting some showers and leaving others confined to the favourable fortnight, so advantage should be taken of this. For instance the Perseid maximum in 1957 had to cope with a Full Moon, whereas in 1961 the Moon was near the Sun and had no effect at all.

Not all maxima occur during the dark hours, of course, and not all are as sharp as the Perseids'. The whole extent of the Quadrantid shower (January 3–4) is confined to a few hours, even though the Z.H.R. is over 40; whereas the Taurids are about equally intense all the time with a rate of 10. Leap year adjustments cause the precise time of maxima to vary each year.

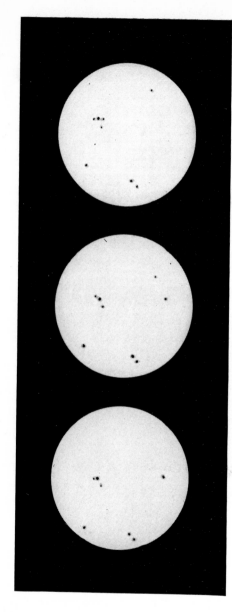

V. Sunspots. Three drawings made by the author on successive days in 1956. 8 × 30 binoculars were used, with a deep green filter in front of each objective. The drift of the spots from west to east, due to the rotation of the Sun, is very obvious.

VI. COMET SEKI-LINES. A drawing made by Richard Dodd on 8th April 1962, using 8 × 30 binoculars. The tail is about 2° long. The star to the right is α Arietis.

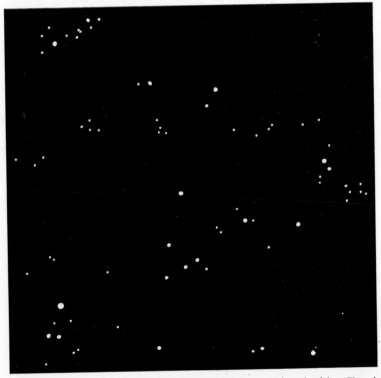

VII. THE HYADES. This open cluster, which is associated with α Tauri (Aldebaran), visible in the lower left-hand corner, is well suited to binoculars. Amateur astronomer John Larard used a 7 × 50 instrument for this drawing.

VIII. THE DOUBLE CLUSTER IN PERSEUS. Although this drawing was made by the author with a 3-inch telescope, high-powered binoculars will give almost as good a view of this grand object.

IX. Aurora: Quiescent Arc. J. R. Bell observed this display from his home in Cumberland on 6th October 1957. This is frequently the early form of the more spectacular display shown below, but on this particular occasion it died away after some hours.

X. Aurora: Draperies. Another drawing made by J. R. Bell, this time on 25th September 1958. It is obvious why this type is often referred to as a 'curtain aurora'.

TABLE IX

Some Important Meteor Showers

There are dozens of discernible showers, but only a small fraction of these give anything in the nature of a worth-while display. The especially active ones are marked with an asterisk.

DATE	SHOWER	REMARKS
January 3–4	Quadrantids*	A very sharp maximum on January 3, which sometimes occurs in daylight. The old constellation of Quadrans Muralis, which gave the shower its name, was in the Draco-Boötes region. Medium speed.
January 17	ϰ Cygnids	A sharp shower of slow meteors, but the radiant is so low that observation is very difficult.
March 10–12	Boötids	Very swift meteors.
April 20–22	Lyrids*	Very swift meteors.
May 6	γ Aquarids	Best seen just before dawn. Very swift; long paths.
July 25–30	δ Aquarids	Slow meteors.
July 27– August 17	Perseids*	A rich shower of very swift meteors. Maximum August 11–12.
October 15–25	Orionids*	Swift meteors. Maximum October 20.
October 26– November 16	Taurids*	Slow meteors. Maximum November 7.
November 17–27	Andromedids	Very slow meteors.
December 10–12	Geminids*	Medium speed; a very rich shower.
December 20–22	Ursids*	Radiant in Ursa Minor.

F

Fireballs

While awaiting the smaller fry of meteor showers, occasional really brilliant objects known as 'fireballs' will be seen. There is no strict definition of a fireball, and people frequently have rather weird ideas about them, confusing them with thunderbolts and other terrestrial phenomena. In actual fact a fireball is simply a large meteor—perhaps as big as a small pebble—and many of them are sporadic.

When a fireball bursts into view, note the beginning and end of the trail as accurately as possible; to do this requires a good knowledge of the sky, but this will come with frequent meteorwatching. If it can then be identified with sightings by other observers, its height and actual flight path can be calculated by a simple piece of triangulation.

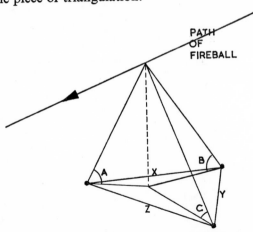

Fig. 21. *The height of a fireball*

Strictly speaking, two observations are sufficient to establish the fireball's position. The probable error is however greatly reduced by the inclusion of a third result.

The principle is simple (Fig. 21). If three different observers see the meteor from different angles, they will each see it projected against a different part of the sky; this will enable the angles A, B and C to be worked out. Then the distances between the observers, X, Y and Z are found, and simple geometry will give the height of the meteor at that particular point in its path. A greater number of sightings will naturally lead to a more accurate result.

Very occasionally a fireball leaves a faint trail of ionized gas in its wake, and it is here that binoculars prove useful, because the behaviour of this train—its drifting or breaking-up—is affected by the little-known high-altitude winds. Sometimes trails last for several minutes, and an account of what happens will be of value.

AURORÆ

Also to be included in the naked-eye category are auroræ, the strange glows that sometimes light up the northern sky in displays ranging from greenish hazes to vivid red curtains. Auroræ are caused by very short-wave particles emitted from sunspots exciting some of the gases in the upper atmosphere, and they are therefore strongly dependent on the sunspot cycle. At the moment (1963) we are near a minimum, so auroræ are in short supply.

Auroræ centre around the north magnetic, not geographic, pole, which at the moment is some 10° west of true north. When a display is seen, first of all note its bearing with reference to a compass or the pole star; then note the time at which anything unusual happens, such as a sudden brightening or the appearance of any unexpected activity. A general description of the display should also be given.

Just occasionally really great displays occur, especially in higher latitudes which are nearer the main auroral region, and these can take amazing forms. Sometimes the light is rayed in a huge arc, shimmering spectrally and casting beams well into the southern sky. Other auroræ take the form of a huge shimmering curtain, apparently waving in some cosmic breeze.

Binoculars are useless for observing auroræ, for their magnification is a positive disadvantage; it blurs the outlines and dilutes the light. They are, however, useful for picking up stars to mark the limit of the display, and notes on its extent at different times are helpful.

For measuring the size of the auroral glow some sort of angular scale must be used. A useful rule to remember is that a foot ruler held at arm's length subtends an angle of about 24°—or 1° per half-inch. If a ruler is not available, from thumb to little finger of the outstretched hand is about 16°. This does at least give some sort of key, though if more accurate results are needed a measuring instrument like a quadrant could easily be made. This would also have obvious applications when measuring fireball trains.

THE ZODIACAL LIGHT

Really vivid auroræ can sometimes be seen from built-up areas, but there is another glow in the sky—a permanent one—which is faint and very difficult to see. This is the Zodiacal Light, caused by sunlight reflected from meteoric particles far out in space. As might be expected it keeps to the region of the ecliptic, appearing as a narrow cone tapering to an apex about 60° away from the Sun.

Because it is so faint it is best seen when the ecliptic makes its greatest angle with the horizon. The law is naturally the same as for Mercury and Venus: a spring evening after sunset, or an autumn morning. The sky, needless to say, must be absolutely dark, and the clearest conditions of air are essential for a good view.

Once again the tropics have the best of it, for the cones, both evening and morning, rise almost vertically into the sky, making the Light a normal sight. Up in Britain the chase is much more exciting, and it is well worth waiting for that chill September morning when the phantom beam crawls slowly up into the black sky.

CHAPTER 6

Beyond the Solar System

Pluto: 5½ light-hours. The nearest star: 4⅓ light-years. The farthest our optical telescopes can see into space: about 4,000 million light-years, possibly more. This is the universe, a tiny local part of which we see every time we glance at the sky on a clear night.

This is a practical book, but practice is not possible without at least some understanding of the objects being observed; a star, for instance, is fascinating not through its own beauty but because of what we know about it, and the same is true of spectacular objects such as nebulæ or star-clusters. So a lightning survey of our astronomical surroundings will not be out of place.

The best way is to use a scale model. Shrinking the Sun to the size of a football (when the Earth becomes about 2 mm. across), we cast around for the nearest star. If we are searching on foot it will take rather a long time, for we shall have to walk no less than four thousand miles. Pluto we shall pass after only a thousand yards. Clearly this is an impracticably large scale if we want to construct the Sun's immediate neighbourhood, for the Earth itself could accommodate only a few stars.

So the scale must be shrunk again, letting the distance between the Sun and the nearest star be one foot. We can then construct a cross-section through our local cluster or 'galaxy' by drawing a circle with a diameter of six miles and filling it with dots one foot apart. Each dot is a star like the Sun, though in practice it would be impossible to make them small enough to fit the scale.

The Galaxy

The Galaxy is in the form of a spiral about 100,000 light-years across, slowly rotating—one revolution takes over 200 million years, so it is quite inappreciable. From the side it looks rather like two fried eggs placed bottoms together, with a conspicuous bulge of stars and gas near the nucleus. Altogether, the Galaxy contains at least 50,000 million stars (some estimates are double this number), and most of them are separated by the same order of distance that splits the Sun from its neighbour.

This, our local star-system, is by no means the only one. Galaxies are scattered throughout space; they are units of the universe in the same way that sand-grains are the units of a sea-shore. And the simile is appropriate enough, for the number of galaxies detectable with our largest instruments runs into the thousand million. Only one, however, is close enough to be at all conspicuous; it appears as a milky blur in the constellation of Andromeda. All the night-sky stars are simply stars in the Sun's neighbourhood, belonging to our own Galaxy.

The Galaxy contains interesting objects other than stars. These are the nebulæ, vast clouds of gas which will one day give birth to stars. One is visible with the naked eye; it is in Orion, below the famous belt, and several more can be picked up with binoculars, though it must be admitted that they are not spectacular.

In addition to these bright nebulæ there are colossal obscuring masses of dark gas and dust, which cannot be seen in themselves but are made visible by the stars they cut off from sight. Several examples can be seen in the Milky Way (which is our view through the thickest part of the Galaxy), appearing as black vacancies among the stars, and they show up much more prominently on long-exposure photographs. From our point of view the most important dark clouds are those which lie between us and the nucleus of the Galaxy, in the direction of

Sagittarius, because the star-density here is so thick that were it not for these tremendous filters their brightness would light up the sky far more effectively than the Full Moon.

THE STARS

In addition to the nebulæ there are three types of stellar object that can come under scrutiny: they are double stars, variable stars, and star clusters.

Double stars

A double star is a star which appears single with the naked eye, but double, or possibly multiple, with a telescope. This distinction naturally depends on the kind of instrument employed, for a double which may tax the powers of binoculars will probably be too easy to be worthy of the name when an astronomical telescope is turned upon it.

The distance between the components is measured in terms of angle, the unit of which is the second of arc ("). A second is $\frac{1}{360}$ part of a degree, so it is obviously a very small angle; the width of a halfpenny $3\frac{1}{2}$ miles away subtends 1", and the Moon's diameter is normally about 2000", or 33' (minutes of arc, or $\frac{1}{60}$ of a degree).

It takes a fair-sized telescope to resolve a double star whose components are only 1" apart, and a great deal depends on their brightness; if one star is much brighter than the other its glare will make separation more difficult. Normally, 8 × 30 binoculars cannot resolve a double much closer than 30"; the unaided eye can split stars down to about 4' apart under very favourable conditions.

Physically there are two distinct types of double star: the optical double, and the binary. An optical double is simply two stars which happen to lie in almost exactly the same line of sight, so that they appear to be almost touching, while in actual fact they are in no way connected. A binary system, on the other hand, consists of two stars revolving around their common centre of gravity. The periods are always long, and may stretch up to hundreds of years, in which case it may take several decades to notice their motion. Amazingly enough, fully a quarter of all the stars in the Galaxy are members of binary systems, and it is perhaps a pity that the Sun chances to be a lone wanderer in space—strictly from the artistic point of view!

Variable stars

However, we can think it fortunate that the Sun's output of light and heat has remained stable for the past millennia, for there is a class of star whose light-output is anything but regular; they are known as variable stars. Once again there are two types. In one, the main one, they are genuinely variable; drastic changes in the star's constitution, which may or may not be regular, cause it to brighten and fade periodically. In the other group the stars are nothing more than binary systems seen edge-on, so that the components mutually occult each other. These 'eclipsing variables' usually have very short periods of just a few days, and they can naturally be predicted with great accuracy.

The genuine variables can also be divided into two classes. In one group they are entirely regular, fluctuating to the second; the most famous of these are the Cepheids, called after their proto-type, δ Cephei, and once again they can be predicted. But the others, the long-period variables, are not so orderly. Their periods are usually about a year, during which time they may brighten to naked-eye visibility, but subsequently dim so drastically that it takes a large telescope to find them. Both periods and brightness are subject to large irregularities, and observation of these variables is a field in which the amateur is still very active indeed. Some of the brighter ones can be observed with binoculars, or even with the naked eye alone.

Observing variable stars

Variable stars are estimated by comparing their brightness or 'magnitude' (page 93) with that of nearby stars whose magnitudes are known. The easiest way is of course to find one of the same brightness, since the magnitude can then be derived without ambiguity. Unfortunately this convenient state of affairs rarely occurs.

In this case select two stars which are slightly brighter and dimmer than the variable, and estimate its position in the sequence. Suppose, for example, that the magnitudes of the comparison stars are 5·4 and 5·8. If the variable is midway in brightness, call it 5·6; if it is closer to one star than the other note it as 5·5 or 5·7 as the case may be.

When making repeated observations of a variable, try always to use the same comparison stars. This will tend to eliminate errors due to colour differences and other effects. Obtaining satisfactory magnitudes for these stars may prove a problem, since there are many catalogues giving their own private values. It is therefore important to quote the source.

The most profitable variable star work open to anyone without a reasonably powerful telescope is that concerned with the really bright variables, such as Betelgeuse in Orion. Since the suitable comparison stars are scattered so widely (and the star's orange hue makes selection still more difficult), binoculars are obviously useless. The naked eye is the only instrument with which they can be tackled, and it is fascinating to watch the slow fluctuations over months or even years.

Star clusters

Star clusters, too, form themselves into two separate types: open and globular. Open clusters are typified by the Pleiades; the stars are well scattered, and binoculars can resolve them without much difficulty. Globular clusters, however, are far more compressed, and even the brightest example available to northern observers—the cluster in Hercules—appears as little more than a circular glow with a low magnification.

Messier's catalogue

There have been many catalogues of nebulæ and clusters. The first reasonably comprehensive one was drawn up by Messier, an Italian comet-seeker, in 1781. Because it was early it contained all the bright objects, and his catalogue references, preceded by the letter M, are still used today. The galaxy in Andromeda, for instance, is M.31. Messier included 103 objects in his list, and they are nearly all visible with binoculars.

THE CONSTELLATIONS

A constellation is simply a specified area of the sky, and most of the northern groups had their rather romantic origins well back in the dim mists of history. They were carefully fitted in with mythological traditions, and by comparison the more modern additions, dating from the seventeenth century, sometimes seem very uncelestial; the southern hemisphere, especially, is decorated with utilitarian articles such as a compass, a furnace, and a painter's easel. But astronomy, mercifully, is more conscious than any other science of its ancestry, and the sky today reflects this confusion of misguided imagination without any attempts at stultifying it with order and logic.

1930 is an important date in constellation history. Before then boundaries had been rather nebulous, and some star catalogues had disagreed as to which star belonged to what constellation; Flamsteed, the first Astronomer Royal, had unintentionally duplicated some stars in his catalogue of 1725, and there were many other similar instances. In this redeeming year, therefore, the International Astronomical Union set down definite constellation boundaries, and also issued a list of standard three-letter abbreviations which are now in universal use (Table X).

TABLE X

The Constellations and Their Abbreviations

Most of the abbreviations are simply the first three letters of the constellation name, but there are exceptions where this might cause confusion or duplication; e.g., Hya, Hydra; Hyi, Hydrus. The abbreviations also act as the genitive, e.g. α Hya.

And	Andromeda	Crv	Corvus
Ant	Antlia	CVn	Canes Venatici
Aps	Apus	Cyg	Cygnus
Aql	Aquila	Del	Delphinus
Aqr	Aquarius	Dor	Dorado
Ara	Ara	Dra	Draco
Arg	Argo	Equ	Equuleus
Ari	Aries	Eri	Eridanus
Aur	Auriga	For	Fornax
Boo	Boötes	Gem	Gemini
Cae	Cælum	Gru	Grus
Cam	Camelopardus	Her	Hercules
Cap	Capricornus	Hor	Horologium
Car	Carina	Hya	Hydra
Cas	Cassiopeia	Hyi	Hydrus
Cen	Centaurus	Ind	Indus
Cep	Cepheus	Lac	Lacerta
Cet	Cetus	Leo	Leo
Cha	Chamæleon	Lep	Lepus
Cir	Circinus	Lib	Libra
CMa	Canis Major	LMi	Leo Minor
CMi	Canis Minor	Lup	Lupus
Cnc	Cancer	Lyn	Lynx
Col	Columba	Lyr	Lyra
Com	Coma Berenices	Men	Mensa
CrA	Corona Australis	Mic	Microscopium
CrB	Corona Borealis	Mon	Monoceros
Crt	Crater	Mus	Musca
Cru	Crux	Nor	Norma

TABLE X (*continued*)

Oct	Octans	Ser	Serpens
Oph	Ophiuchus	Sex	Sextans
Ori	Orion	Sge	Sagitta
Pav	Pavo	Sgr	Sagittarius
Peg	Pegasus	Tau	Taurus
Per	Perseus	Tel	Telescopium
Phe	Phœnix	TrA	Triangulum Australe
Pic	Pictor	Tri	Triangulum
PsA	Piscis Austrinus	Tuc	Tucana
Psc	Pisces	UMa	Ursa Major
Pup	Puppis	UMi	Ursa Minor
Pyx	Pyxis	Vel	Vela
Ret	Reticulum	Vir	Virgo
Scl	Sculptor	Vol	Volans
Sco	Scorpius	Vul	Vulpecula
Sct	Scutum		

Star identification

So many catalogues have been issued that star identification is, frankly, in a state of confusion. Luckily the brighter stars are catered for by two systems, those of Bayer (1603) and Flamsteed, and binocular work is unlikely to require reference to any of the more advanced modern catalogues.

Bayer used the Greek alphabet, and his general idea was to label the stars in each constellation in order of brightness; in the constellation Lyra, for instance, α Lyræ is the brightest, with β and γ coming second and third respectively. This system, of course, limits itself to the 24 brightest stars, and in any case Bayer was not systematic; he labelled Ursa Major's seven main stars in simple order of position, and there are other instances also. Nevertheless, the alphabetical listing is so well established that it will never be changed now.

When reference is made to the fainter but still naked-eye stars, Flamsteed's numbers are used. In his catalogue he numbered every naked-eye star in each constellation not in order of brightness, but in order of position, from west to east. A small constellation might therefore muster only twenty or thirty stars, while a rambling one might reach a hundred or more. Flamsteed numbered every star, including the ones Bayer had catalogued, but in these cases the Bayer letter is always used. This double system may appear confusing at first, but both are logical, and for amateur work they are preferable to modern catalogues which ignore constellations altogether and simply work round from west to east.

The old Arab astronomers were very keen on naming the stars. Many of these names have been handed down, but only a handful are in popular use; α Lyræ, for instance, is always referred to as Vega. Simple names like these are all very well, but it is obviously much easier to talk about γ Libræ than *Zuben el Hakrabi*, especially on a frosty night.

Variable stars have a special system of nomenclature. The brighter ones, whose variability might have been undetected when Bayer and Flamsteed drew up their catalogues, mostly retain their original references; thus α Orionis is a variable, and so is 15 Monocerotis. Other fainter variables have been given letters, according to the constellation, beginning with R and working through to Z (R Persei, W Andromedæ, etc.). However this allows for only nine variables per constellation, which is often not enough, so there follows the cumbersome system of continuing with RR, RS, RT . . . RZ, after which comes SR, SS, ST, etc. This suffices for all the brighter and more important variables.

The responsibility for starting with R rests with Bayer, who obviously had rather modest ideas on the subject of variable stars. He would be delighted to see how slavishly modern science has adhered to his principle!

STAR MAGNITUDES

Star brightnesses are classified in grades or 'magnitudes', a misleading unit since it has nothing at all to do with their size. The magnitude scale had its rough beginnings with the Greek astronomer Ptolemy; he called the brightest stars 'first magnitude' stars, the faintest, sixth magnitude. The invention of the telescope naturally brought fainter stars into view, the limit of the 200-inch being near the 21st magnitude, while the whole scale has been tightened into mathematical lines. A difference of five magnitudes between two stars means that one is exactly 100 times as bright as the other, while one magnitude means a ratio of about $2\frac{1}{2}$, the exact factor being $\sqrt[5]{100}$.

TABLE XI

Standard Star Magnitudes

Note that Polaris is slightly variable. Canopus has been included although it is too far south to be visible from British latitudes.

	STAR	MAGNITUDE
α	CMa (Sirius)	−1·44
α	Arg (Canopus)	−0·86
α	Boo (Arcturus)	−0·06
α	Lyr (Vega)	0·00
β	Ori (Rigel)	0·08
α	Aur (Capella)	0·21
α	CMi (Procyon)	0·36
α	Sco (Antares)	0·92
α	Vir (Spica)	0·98
α	Per	1·90
α	UMi (Polaris)	2·10
β	Dra	2·99
ζ	Her	3·00
γ	CrB	3·93
δ	Cet	4·04
ρ	UMa	4·99
ε	UMi	5·04

Table XI gives the magnitudes of some naked-eye stars, to help in classification. The three brightest stars in the sky, Sirius, Canopus and Arcturus, actually have negative values, while Vega is conveniently exactly zero. Planetary magnitudes vary according to their distance from the Earth and Sun; Venus, the brightest, can reach −4·4, and Mars can reach −2·8 at a perihelic opposition. Uranus, lingering near the threshold of naked-eye visibility, is about 5·7.

In a first-class sky 30 mm. binoculars should be able to reach about mag. 9, but it depends so much on visual acuity and other factors that there is no point in defining a limit.

CELESTIAL POSITIONS

When we wish to define the position of a celestial object, the method used is basically the same as that used by a geographer in defining a point on the Earth's surface: by latitude and longitude. The celestial equivalent of latitude is Declination (Dec.);

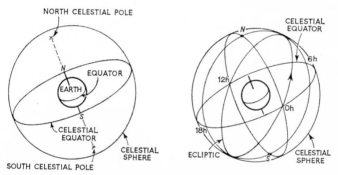

Fig. 22. *The celestial sphere*

that of longitude is Right Ascension (R.A.). Dec. is measured in degrees, north and south, but R.A. is measured in hours, from 0 to 24, for a reason which will become clear.

The celestial sphere

The easiest way of understanding celestial positions is by inventing a couple of fictions (Fig. 22). First of all, suppose that instead of being scattered throughout space the stars are all equidistant, attached to a sphere whose centre is the Earth: the 'celestial sphere'. Then, instead of insisting that the Earth spins from west to east, pretend that the celestial globe spins from east to west. There is a precedent for this; all motion is relative, and in absolute terms we can speak of the Sun and stars moving round the Earth without being accused of Ptolemaic tendencies.

So with the celestial sphere revolving round us once in 24 hours, it is easy to fix certain points on it. First of all extend the Earth's axis to cut it, which produces the north and south celestial poles. It so happens that there is a bright star very near the north pole, though the southern hemisphere is not so fortunate.

Similarly, by extending the plane of the equator, we can produce a great circle on the sphere: the celestial equator. A moment's thought will show that any star on the celestial equator must pass directly overhead to an observer on the terrestrial equator, while observers in other latitudes will see the equator inclined lower and lower in the sky, until at the poles it runs round the horizon and the appropriate celestial pole is overhead.

These references can now be used to define a star's position. Its latitude, or declination, is the number of degrees it is north or south of the celestial equator (north positive, south negative). R.A., however, is a little more complex. Lines of longitude can be drawn from pole to pole, but a starting-point is needed on the celestial equator from which reckoning can start. Terrestrial longitude suffered from the same trouble until Greenwich was internationally recognized as 0°.

The Sun comes in here. It was shown on page 46 how it crosses the celestial equator at the two equinoxes; at the vernal going north, and at the autumnal going south. The spot at which it crosses going north, the vernal equinox, defines the zero of R.A., the starting-point from which celestial longitude is measured. Going eastwards, the equator is divided into 24 equal sections of one hour each, since it takes 24 hours for the sphere to revolve once.

Fig. 22 also shows the celestial sphere with the ecliptic drawn in, together with some lines of R.A. If we follow the annual path of the Sun, we find that when it is in 0° it is spring; in 6^h

it is midsummer; in 12^h it is autumn, and in 18^h it is midwinter. The ecliptic is inclined to the equator at the Earth's axial tilt of $23\frac{1}{2}°$, so the four solar positions may be defined fully as R.A. 0^h, Dec. $0°$; R.A. 6^h, Dec. $+23\frac{1}{2}°$; R.A. 12^h, Dec. $0°$; and R.A. 18^h, Dec. $-23\frac{1}{2}°$. Star positions are given in the same way, though of course they stay the same from year to year.

THE SEASONS

There remains the explanation of why different seasons provide different constellations. The answer lies in the simple reason that the stars can be seen only at night; as we move round the Sun, we see them from a slightly different angle.

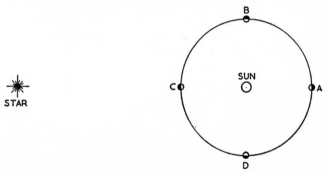

Fig. 23. *Seasonal shift of the constellations* (Not to scale)

Fig. 23 should make it clear. Suppose a star is being observed. When the Earth is in position A the Sun is in the region of the star, and it cannot be seen. At B (three months later), the star makes an angle of 90° with the Sun and can be seen in the early morning. By the time the Earth has reached C it is more or less between the Sun and the star, which is due south at midnight, like a planet at opposition. After that it slips further into the evening sky until the Sun moves into its region again.

From this it is obvious that we see the star in the same place a little earlier each night (since night and day are defined by reference to the Sun, *not* to the stars). The exact amount is easy to calculate: it is 24 hours multiplied by $\frac{1}{365}$, the sector of its

97   G

orbit through which the Earth moves in one day. This comes out to about four minutes, which means that a star or constellation arrives at its previous position four minutes earlier each night.

SIDEREAL TIME

To complete this perhaps difficult section there is the matter of sidereal time or star time. The Sun, our civil timekeeper, returns to its old position in exactly 24 hours (neglecting slight variations). A star takes four minutes less, so that a sidereal day is in fact only 23 hours 56 minutes long, and the sidereal time at any instant is defined as the R.A. which is due south at that instant.

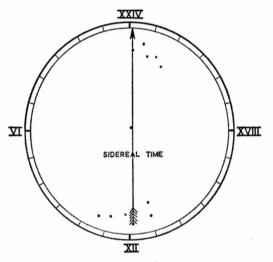

Fig. 24. *The cosmic clock*

Note that the celestial dial is numbered in an anti-clockwise direction.

An example may help here. On December 21 the Sun is in R.A. 18^h, and at noon it is due south. So the sidereal time at noon on that day is 18 hours. By March 21 the noon sidereal time is 0 hours, the difference slipping away all the time. Table XII gives conversions for 24^h U.T. (midnight) to sidereal time throughout the year.

Beyond the Solar System

TABLE XII

Sidereal Time at Midnight

The table gives the sidereal time at midnight (24^h U.T.) on each of the dates mentioned. To obtain the S.T. for one hour earlier, subtract an hour; later, add an hour.

Sidereal time gains on G.M.T. at the rate of $3 \cdot 9$ minutes per day, from which it follows that S.T. at midnight on any given day is the same as that at 23^h U.T. a fortnight later; this, of course, is why the constellations are slowly displaced from east to west.

DATE	SIDEREAL TIME	DATE	SIDEREAL TIME
January 5	7^h	July 7	19^h
13	$7\frac{1}{2}$	15	$19\frac{1}{2}$
21	8	22	20
28	$8\frac{1}{2}$	30	$20\frac{1}{2}$
February 5	9	August 6	21
13	$9\frac{1}{2}$	14	$21\frac{1}{2}$
20	10	22	22
28	$10\frac{1}{2}$	29	$22\frac{1}{2}$
March 7	11	September 6	23
15	$11\frac{1}{2}$	13	$23\frac{1}{2}$
22	12	21	0
29	$12\frac{1}{2}$	29	$\frac{1}{2}$
April 6	13	October 6	1
14	$13\frac{1}{2}$	14	$1\frac{1}{2}$
22	14	21	2
29	$14\frac{1}{2}$	29	$2\frac{1}{2}$
May 7	15	November 6	3
15	$15\frac{1}{2}$	13	$3\frac{1}{2}$
22	16	21	4
30	$16\frac{1}{2}$	29	$4\frac{1}{2}$
June 6	17	December 6	5
14	$17\frac{1}{2}$	14	$5\frac{1}{2}$
22	18	21	6
29	$18\frac{1}{2}$	29	$6\frac{1}{2}$

From this table it is easy to find when a certain star is well placed for observation. Find its R.A. in a star atlas, and then run down the list of sidereal times to find the appropriate value. On that date the star is due south at midnight, and conditions will be favourable for a couple of months on either side of that date.

The matter of celestial positions and sidereal time is notoriously hard to understand. The quickest way of learning it is with a planetarium; failing that, a fortnight's study of the sky will reveal the gradual swing of the stars and the creeping of the Sun. Astronomy is essentially an outdoor pursuit, and binocular users can take heart from the fact that it is better to see a little that is direct rather than a great deal that is second-hand.

THE STAR MAPS

Nine star maps accompany the following description of the sky at different seasons of the year. With the exception of the first, which shows the region around the north celestial pole, they are in pairs covering each quarter of the sky north of latitude $-30°$. They include stars down to the 5th magnitude, as well as interesting objects referred to in the text.

Table XIII

The Greek Alphabet

α	Alpha	ν	Nu
β	Beta	ξ	Xi
γ	Gamma	o	Omicron
δ	Delta	π	Pi
ε	Epsilon	ρ	Rho
ζ	Zeta	σ	Sigma
η	Eta	τ	Tau
θ	Theta	υ	Upsilon
ι	Iota	φ	Phi
κ	Kappa	χ	Chi
λ	Lambda	ψ	Psi
μ	Mu	ω	Omega

CHAPTER 7

Spring Stars

(Boötes, Canes Venatici, Coma Berenices, Corona Borealis, Corvus, Crater, Hydra, Leo, Leo Minor, Libra, Sextans, Ursa Major, Ursa Minor, Virgo)

After each constellation is given the approximate date on which it is due south at 22ʰ U.T. This gives some guide to the best time for observation.

Boötes, The Herdsman (June 2; MAP 2)
With its leading orange star, Arcturus, Boötes heralds the coming of summer. There is always the comfort, when seeing Arcturus rising in the east, that winter has not long to go; and by the time it disappears into the evening twilight the long summer days have arrived.

Easily found by continuing the curve of stars δ–η in Ursa Major, Boötes looks rather like a kite with Arcturus dangling from its tail. Look at δ, forming the left-hand corner; it is a rather difficult double, mags. 3 and 7·4, 105″. Much easier is μ, mags. 4 and 6·7, 108″. The fainter star is itself a close binary with a period of some 230 years.

Also look at θ, near Ursæ Majoris; it is in a pretty field.

There is a variable, R, near ε. The magnitude range is from 6 to 13, period 222 days. Even closer to ε, and easily picked up, is the strange variable 34 (Flamsteed's number), which fluctuates from 5·2 to 6·1 with no semblance of a period. This is well worth watching with binoculars.

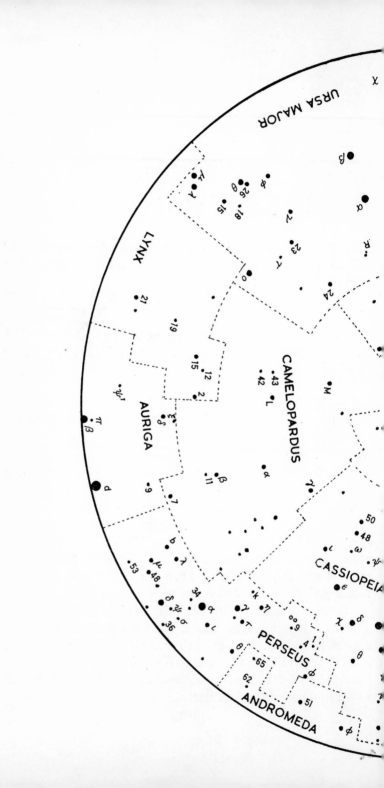

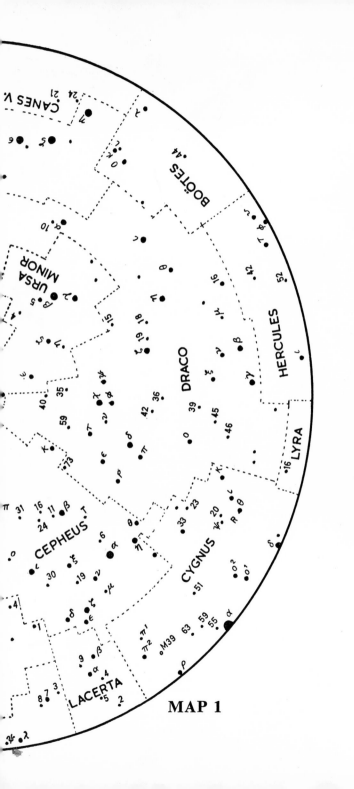

MAP 1

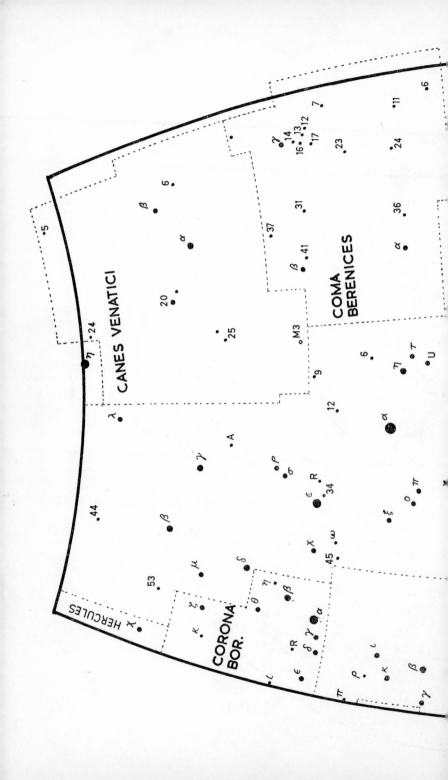

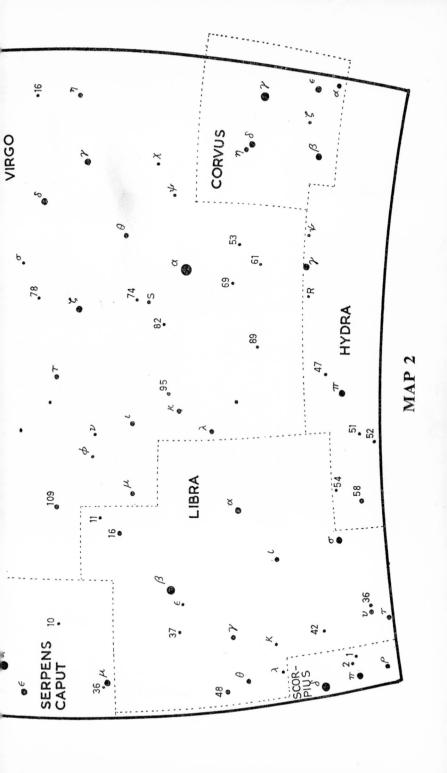

MAP 2

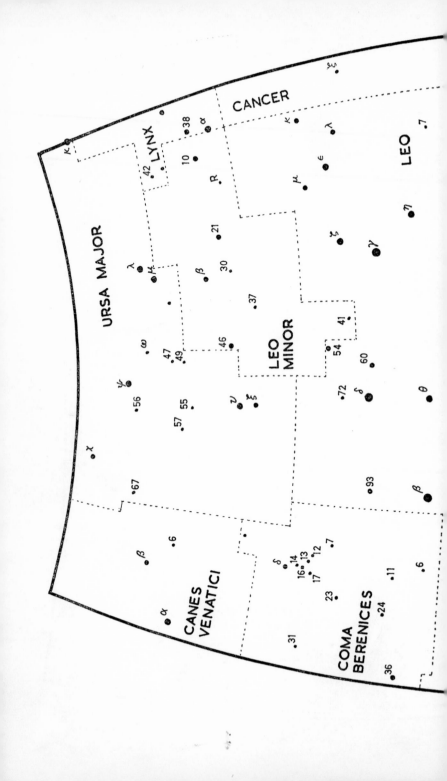

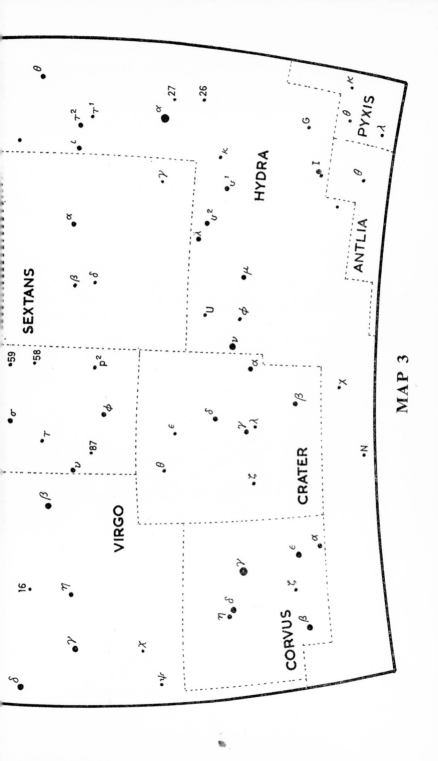

MAP 3

Canes Venatici, The Hunting Dogs (May 7; MAP 2)
Very easily found, beneath the canopy formed by δ–η Ursæ
Majoris. It contains an interesting globular star-cluster, M.3,
which can be seen as a faint blurred spot in binoculars. With
large telescopes it can be resolved into stars.

Coma Berenices, Berenice's Hair (May 2; MAP 2)
Lies roughly in the triangle formed by α Canum Venaticum,
Arcturus, and β Leonis. It could really be called a star-cluster
instead of a more normal constellation.

Coma, and its southern neighbour Virgo, contain between them literally hundreds of faint, distant galaxies; it so
happens that a great number of them are clustered together in
this particular line of sight. It seems that galaxies were formed
in colossal clusters in the same way as many of the stars they
contain are clustered together.

Many people misleadingly refer to them as 'extra-galactic
nebulæ', or just simply 'nebulæ'; remember that they are nothing at all to do with nebulæ, which are gaseous clouds within
our own Galaxy.

Corona Borealis, The Northern Crown (June19; MAPS 2 and 5)
A distinctive little constellation immediately to the east of
Boötes, consisting of a semicircle of faint stars embracing its
mag. 2 leader. Note ν, a wide double, mags. 4·8 and 5·1, 370″.

Corona has an important variable star, R, which ranges from
5·8 to 12·5 in a very irregular manner; usually it stays bright
for a year or two before fading very quickly. It is certainly well
worth watching.

Corvus and Crater, The Crow and The Cup
    (April 20; MAPS 2 and 3)
Two little constellations south of Virgo, and therefore always
rather low in the sky. Corvus, to the east, is the brighter of the
two; it has a conspicuous quadrangle which includes two mag. 2
stars, but they both lack anything worth chasing with binoculars.

Hydra, The Water Snake (April 15; MAPS 2, 3 and 8)
A menace of a constellation, spreading itself through 100° of sky from Libra to Cancer. It has two interesting variables, U (4·5 to 6·0, irregular) and R (4·0 to 10·1, 415 days), but because of their isolated positions they are difficult to pick up except when bright.

Leo, The Lion (April 1; MAP 3)
Large and obvious, and remarkable in having a definite resemblance to its namesake; the name and general form of a lion is very clear. Its leading star, Regulus, lies almost on the ecliptic.

ε is attractive in binoculars, though its two companions are hardly close enough to make it a genuine triple star. Try τ, mags. 5·5 and 7, 90″; or, much more difficult, 7, mags. 6 and 8, 42″. The main variable is R, 5·0 to 10·5, period 312 days.

Paradoxically enough, bright variable stars are often harder to observe properly than the usual faint variable. The reason is the lack of suitable comparison stars, and β Leonis is a good example. It is suspected by some to be slowly variable (probably in terms of decades), and the only way to check up is by naked-eye estimation against other nearby stars. Unfortunately there is only one suitably placed: γ Leonis. It would be a waiting game, but it might be worth while glancing at the two every now and then. At present γ is fractionally brighter.

Leo Minor (March 23; MAP 3)
A literally minor constellation above Leo's head. Its one object of possible interest is the variable R, 6·2 to 12·0, period 370 days.

Libra, The Scales (June 10; MAP 2)
A dull region of the sky between Ophiuchus and Virgo, containing the celebrated 'green' star β. In large telescopes it is undoubtedly greenish, but binoculars are unlikely to give it any distinctive tinge. Many star colours are very elusive indeed, different observers all preferring their own private hues, and it

depends a great deal on the aperture of the telescope; there is a certain ideal brightness for colour estimates.

Sextans, The Sextant (March 22; MAP 3)
A faint asterism beneath Leo's forepaws; nothing here of interest.

Ursa Major, The Great Bear (April 11; MAPS 1 and 3)
The standard landmark (or should we say skymark?) of the northern hemisphere, and it needs no introduction. As a constellation, however, it lacks anything very spectacular for observers with binoculars; its main bid for fame lies in the star ζ. Good eyes will reveal another much fainter star about a third of the Moon's diameter to the north, and this fainter star is known as Alcor. ζ itself is usually called Mizar, and the Mizar-Alcor system is a well-known naked-eye test.

If Alcor is invisible, it may be because there is slight haze around. At any rate, turn binoculars on to it; if conditions are reasonable they will reveal a faint star between the pair, much too dim to be visible with the unaided eye. There is a mystery here. The old Arab astronomers, who gave Mizar and Alcor their names, considered Alcor to be a very exacting test of vision. It is certainly no such test today. Has Alcor brightened since their day, or has this fainter object dimmed down below the threshold of visibility and had its name accidentally transferred? We know that some stars vary in brightness over excessively long periods, and it is not impossible that Mizar's 8th magnitude companion is in fact a variable star.

Of more subtle interest is T Ursæ Majoris, a variable forming the northern apex of a roughly equilateral triangle with δ and ε. The magnitude range is from 5·5 to 13·1, so that at maximum it can be picked up with the naked eye, while at minimum it requires a powerful telescope to detect it at all. The period is 254 days.

Another variable is R, 6·0 to 13·0, period 298 days. It can be easily picked up near a little group of stars.

Ursa Minor, The Little Bear (June 13; MAP 1)

The Great Bear's smaller brother, it is rather barren ground for binoculars. α is, of course, the Pole Star, and is very slightly variable—a point overlooked by astronomers some years ago when they used it as a standard magnitude star for an exact classification of star brightnesses!

Both the Bears are circumpolar in the British Isles, which means that they are so close to the pole that they never actually reach the horizon. The other constellations which never set are Camelopardus, Cassiopeia, Cepheus and Draco.

Virgo, The Virgin (May 10; MAP 2)

A fine open constellation on that part of the ecliptic between Leo and Libra. α is a conspicuous white star, Spica, forming a triangle with β Leonis and Arcturus. The only interesting object, however, is the variable S, easily found among a little group of stars to the north of Spica (5·6 to 12·5, period 372 days).

CHAPTER 8

Summer Stars

(Aquila, Capricornus, Cygnus, Delphinus, Draco, Equuleus, Hercules, Lyra, Ophiuchus, Sagitta, Sagittarius, Scorpius, Scutum, Serpens, Vulpecula)

Aquila, The Eagle (August 15; MAP 4)

Altair, Aquila's leader, forms the southern apex of the 'summer triangle', the other corners being marked by Vega (α Lyræ) and Deneb (α Cygni). This huge triangle forms a landmark in the summer sky. Aquila itself lies on the celestial equator, to the east of Ophiuchus.

η is worth watching. It is a Cepheid variable (called after the prototype, δ Cephei) and belongs to a strange class of stars whose luminosity fluctuates like clockwork—though perhaps this is doing them an injustice. η ranges from mag. 3·7 to 4·5 in a total period of 7 days 4 hours 14 minutes. It spends about 40 hours at maximum brilliancy and 30 hours at minimum, and there are plenty of nearby stars to check it against.

Aquila's main long-period variable is R, slightly west of the line joining δ and ζ; the range is mag. 5·8 to 11·8, period 310 days. There is also another variable V, which though only reaching mag. 6·5 at maximum has a spectacular red hue. It is easily found then, very close to λ.

As a constellation the western border of Aquila is worth sweeping for its Milky Way star-fields, though they are nothing like so spectacular as those further up in the Cygnus region.

112

Summer Stars

Capricornus, The Sea-Goat (September 8; MAPS 4 and 7)

An obscure constellation south of Aquarius; its leading stars, α and β, are found roughly by continuing a line from Altair through θ Aquilæ.

α itself is an easy naked-eye double, mags. 3·2 and 4·2, 6′ 16″; the components are called α¹ and α² respectively. They are not physically connected in any way; α¹ is fifteen times nearer the Sun—about 100 light-years away.

β is also a very wide double, mags. 3·3 and 6·2, 3′ 30″. The bright star has a deep yellowish cast, the fainter one being blue-white.

Cygnus, The Swan (August 30; MAPS 1 and 4)

Here we come across some superb Milky Way fields; anyone with a black sky and Cygnus in the zenith needs only a pair of binoculars to be on speaking terms, so to speak, with the Galaxy. Stars crowd into view in seemingly endless patterns, and every night reveals new wonders.

Cygnus is in the form of a cross (it is often referred to as the Northern Cross), and for a small telescope β, the most southerly star, is probably the most beautiful double in the sky: mags. 3·0 and 5·3, 35″, rich yellow and blue. Oddly enough some people see the fainter star green, and it demonstrates, once again, how no two people ever see the same thing through a telescope!

o² (the northern star of the conspicuous naked-eye double to the west of α (Deneb) is well worth looking at. It is a triple star, and a fine sight in binoculars.

On the opposite side of Deneb is the fainter star 61 Cygni. This is a double, though not in binoculars; it was also the first star to have its distance measured (in 1838), and the pair are known to have a massive planet circling round them. For these reasons it is something of a museum-piece.

M.39 is an open cluster repaying the search. Of the variables χ is the most interesting; it ranges from mag. 4·2 to 13·7, period 410 days. There are also R (6·0 to 13·9, 426 days), X (5·9 to 7·0, 16·4 days—a Cepheid), W (5·0 to 6·7, 132 days), and a short-period one: SU (6.2 to 7·0, 3·8 days).

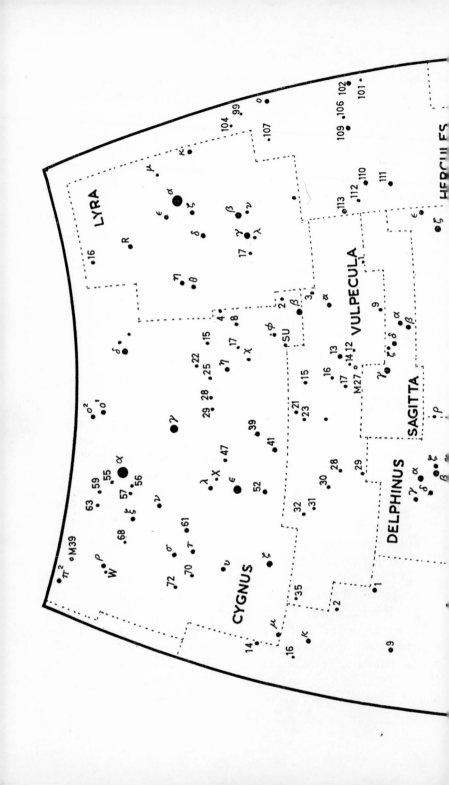

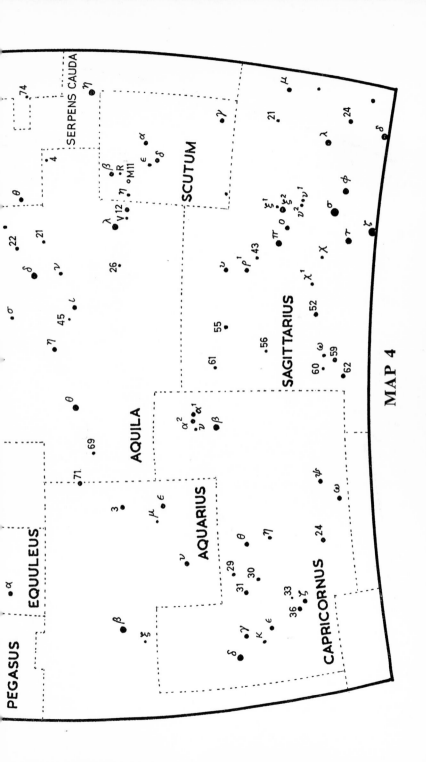

MAP 4

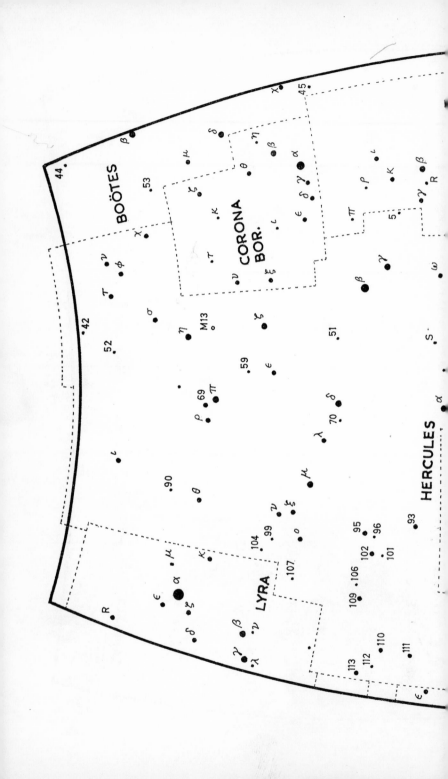

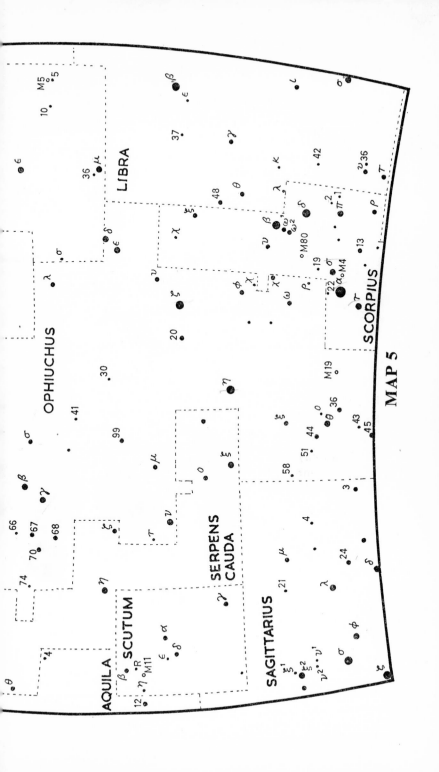

MAP 5

Delphinus, The Dolphin (August 31; MAP 4)
A small constellation between Pegasus and Aquila, but very easy to identify.

Draco, The Dragon (May 25; MAP 1)
A faint, straggling constellation. The bulk of it lies between Cygnus and Ursa Major; it contains nothing of interest.

Equuleus, The Little Horse (September 8; MAP 4)
South of Delphinus. A small and uninteresting constellation.

Hercules (July 13; MAPS 4 and 5)
Large but unremarkable with the naked eye, midway between Corona and Lyra. There are no binocular doubles, but α, a red star almost in Ophiuchus, is of interest; it varies irregularly, between mags. 3 and 4, and there are plenty of suitable comparison stars. Fairly near is S, ranging from 5·9 to 12·5 in about 300 days.

Hercules contains the finest globular star-cluster to be seen in the northern sky: M.13, midway between η and ζ and easily swept up with binoculars. Unfortunately they show it only as a misty spot. Said to be a glorious object in a moderate telescope, I have always found it a distinct disappointment, though it is undeniably the most spectacular example of its kind visible in northern latitudes.

Lyra, The Lyre (August 1; MAPS 4 and 5)
Small, but for its size one of the brightest constellations, especially as α (Vega) is the most brilliant star in the late summer sky. It passes almost overhead, and its blue-white hue is unmistakable.

It is worth remembering, when looking at Vega, that the Sun and its attendant planets are all moving towards it at a steady 13 miles per second. Of course this tremendous velocity is a mere crawl when compared with Vega's distance of 25 light-years or 150 million million miles, and in any case the star's own motion is carrying it out of the way. In some ways this is a pity, for Vega is 50 times as bright as the Sun, has $2\frac{1}{2}$ times the diameter, and would altogether provide a spectacular subject for film newsreels in A.D. 30,000,000.

Between Vega and β Cygni are a pair of stars, β and γ Lyræ. β is an 'eclipsing variable'; it is a very close binary system seen edgewise, so that the two components periodically occult each other. The light consequently varies in intensity during their period of 12 days 21 hours 45 minutes, from mag. 3·4 to 4·1. The actual components are unfortunately too close together to be seen individually, even in the largest telescopes.

Between β and γ is the famous Ring Nebula, which is invisible with binoculars.

Lyra also boasts the 'double-double' ε, which together with ζ forms a little triangle with Vega. Perfect eyesight, or failing that a glance through binoculars, will reveal ε to consist of two stars about $3\frac{1}{2}'$ apart. Then turn an astronomical telescope on to the pair, and they both divide into almost identical doubles. They are both binary systems, and what is more the two systems are physically connected, $ε^1$ and $ε^2$ revolving around each other in an immensely long period, probably something like a million years.

Ophiuchus, The Serpent-Bearer (July 10; MAP 5)
Lying as it does in a rich part of the Milky Way, immediately south of Hercules, Ophiuchus is well worth casual sweeping; some of the star-fields are very fine. The only interesting single object is the cluster M.19, between θ and Antares, and therefore low in the sky.

Sagitta, The Arrow (August 15; MAP 4)
A small, compact constellation just to the north of Altair, and therefore easily found. It lies in the Milky Way and is worth sweeping.

Sagittarius, The Archer (August 10; MAPS 4 and 5)
One of the penalties of living in high northern latitudes is that Sagittarius, with its magnificent Milky Way clouds (it lies

in the direction of the centre of the Galaxy), never rises completely above the southern horizon, and even at its highest it is in the short twilight nights of summer. We are therefore reduced to tantalizing glimpses of some of the clusters and star-clouds that collect thickly in this part of the sky. The best way is to sweep over the whole region, especially that part immediately south of Scutum.

Scorpius, The Scorpion (July 3; MAP 5)

If it were higher in the sky Scorpius would be one of the grandest constellations of all, for it pays host to some dense areas of the Milky Way. As it is, however, atmospheric dimming makes it far inferior to Cygnus. Nevertheless it contains its complement of star-clusters: M.4, near α (Antares), a brilliant red star; and M.80, between Antares and β, considered by some to be the richest mass of stars in the whole sky. Unfortunately it is too dense to be resolved with binoculars.

Scutum, The Shield (August 1; MAPS 4 and 5)

A faint asterism north of Sagittarius, but its three principal stars are easily recognized. It contains an irregular variable R, which ranges from mag. 4·7 to 7·8, just south of β. In the same region is a diffuse cluster, M.11, which offers no challenge to binoculars.

Serpens, The Serpent (June 20, July 25; MAPS 4 and 5)

This constellation is divided into two separate minor figures: Serpens Cauda (the body) and Serpens Caput (the head), on the east and west flanks of Ophiuchus. The stars, however, are labelled as though belonging to the single constellation of Serpens. Note the variable R, easily found between β and γ; it varies from mag. 5·5 to 13·4 in a rough period of 360 days. There is also a fine globular cluster, M.5, which binoculars will show as a patch of light.

Vulpecula, The Fox (August 25; MAP 4)

A very faint constellation lying roughly between β and ζ

Cygni. It might be worth looking up M.27, just south of 14 Vulpeculæ, a nebula whose appearance in long-exposure photographs has earned it the name 'dumb-bell'. In binoculars, however, it is merely a tiny spot.

CHAPTER 9

Autumn Stars

(Andromeda, Aquarius, Aries, Cassiopeia, Cepheus, Cetus, Lacerta, Pegasus, Perseus, Pisces, Triangulum)

Andromeda (November 10; MAPS 6 and 7)

Oddly obscure as a constellation, but its four main stars (α, δ, β, and γ, in that order) extend from the Great Square of Pegasus to α Persei, and are quite unmistakable.

Andromeda contains the only external galaxy in the northern hemisphere that is visible with the naked eye: the confusingly-named 'great Andromeda nebula'. A nebula, remember, is a cloud of gas within our own Galaxy, and therefore is relatively close. The Andromeda 'nebula' is in fact a galaxy, though naturally it appears fuzzy and nebular to the eye, and even in a big telescope.

It is bright enough to be found very easily, but there is a convenient pointer. First find β Andromedæ; north of it is μ, north again is ν, and closely north-west is the galaxy, M.31. Binoculars show it as a diffuse misty blur, and it requires long-exposure photography to resolve some of the stars in it. But it is a sobering thought to reflect that the light reaching our eyes today started on its journey nearly two million years ago. By these standards all the other objects in the night sky are almost terrifyingly near.

Immediately south is another much fainter object, M.32, which is actually a satellite galaxy of M.31. We have analogous companions in the form of the two Magellanic Clouds, which are unfortunately in the far south latitudes.

The variable R, near M.31, has a period of 410 days and a magnitude range from 5·6 to 15.

Aquarius, The Water-Bearer (September 25; MAPS 4 and 7)
A rather rambling constellation, with its brightest stars huddled in one corner, forming a conspicuous group known as the Water Jar to the south-east of θ Pegasi. Sweep downwards from this curiously-named asterism for the explanation; there is a faint stream of stars running southwards towards the horizon, a stream which someone's powerful imagination translated into water.

There is a long-period variable, R, near ω²: range of magnitude 6·0 to 11, period 380 days.

Aries, The Goat (November 30; MAP 6)
A conspicuous little group to the south of the Andromeda line, forming a rough equilateral triangle with α and γ Andromedæ. Nothing for binoculars, though in a telescope γ is a beautiful double.

Cassiopeia (November 9; MAPS 1 and 7)
Circumpolar, on the opposite side of the Pole Star from Ursa Major. Its 'W' configuration is unmistakable.

Cassiopeia lies in a rich part of the Milky Way, and the sweeping here is very fine. And although it is lacking in binocular doubles or clusters, it contains two of the most interesting variables in the northern sky: α and γ Cassiopeiæ. α has been credited with a range of mag. 2 to 3, but this seems to be a slight exaggeration; 2 to 2·5 is probably more reliable. There is a very rough period of 80 days.

γ is more remarkable, because it has no semblance of a period and ranges from 1·7 to 3·4. Both these stars deserve careful attention, the more so since there are three comparison stars nearby: β (2·4); δ (2·8); and ε (3·4). The Pole Star is also handy; its magnitude is 2·1.

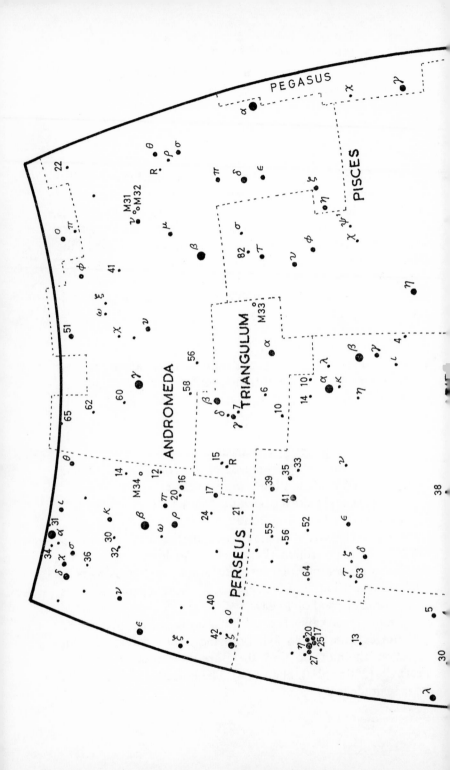

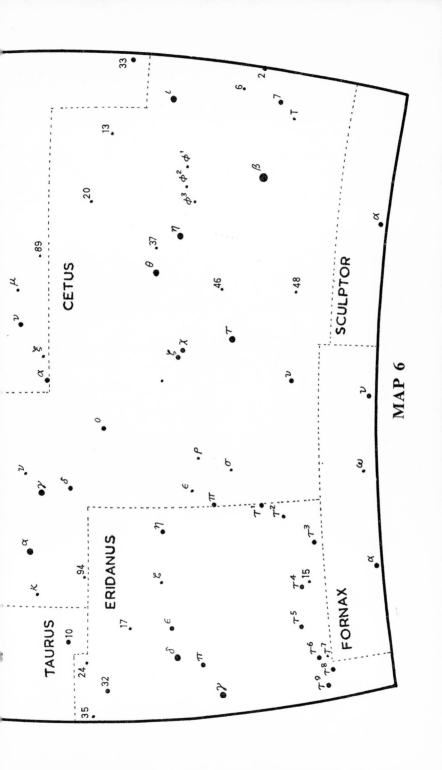

MAP 6

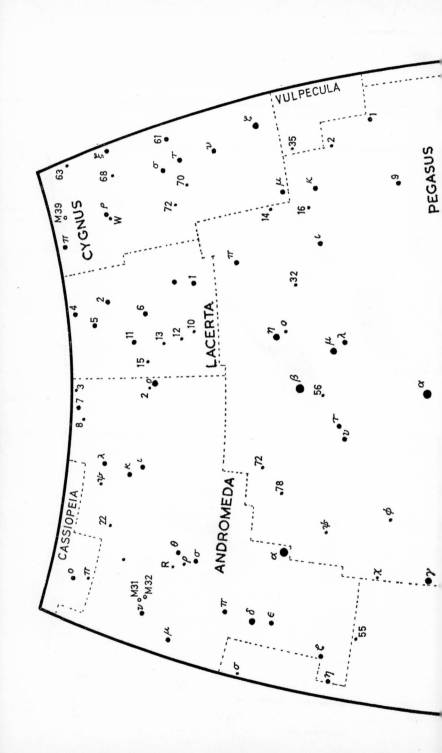

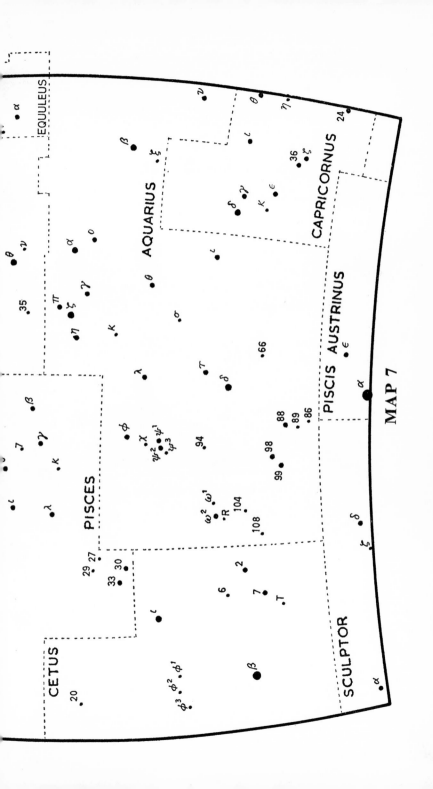

MAP 7

Cassiopeia and Ursa Major between them constitute the Cosmic Clock (Fig. 24). Draw a line from β Cassiopeiæ through the Pole Star to γ Ursæ Majoris. The angle this line makes with the horizon indicates the sidereal time on a celestial 24-hour dial, and with practice it can be estimated to within about half an hour. When the hand is vertical it is, conveniently, 0^h.

Cepheus (October 29; MAP 1)
A rather barren circumpolar constellation pointed to by α and β Cassiopeiæ. Its main interest is δ, the prototype of the Cepheid variables, which ranges from mag. 3·6 to 4·3 in a period of 5 days 8 hours 48 minutes.

μ Cephei is another variable, but this time an irregular one; the range is approximately 3·7 to 4·7, and the period is about six years. It is worth finding for its striking red tint alone. Another variable is T, which is not too easy to find except near maximum: mag. 5·2 to 9·5, period 390 days.

Cetus, The Whale (November 15; MAPS 6 and 7)
A straggling equatorial constellation, marking a very dull region of the sky between Aquarius and Taurus. However, there is one compensation: it contains Mira (ο Ceti), the 'Wonder Star', which is certainly the most spectacular variable in the sky.

Mira is the usual long-period variable, with a very rough period of 330 days; it is the magnitude variation which is unusual. With normal maxima about mag. 3·5, minima between 8·5 and 9·5, it has occasionally risen as high as 1·7, while at other times it has managed to struggle up only to 5. Clearly, something very unusual is going on; and since Mira is entirely unpredictable it is certainly worth watching, especially since binoculars can cover its whole range.

Maxima usually last about a month. It spends some five months at minimum, and the rise is usually faster than the fall.

Another utterly irregular variable, this time in period, is T, in the south-west corner. Its magnitude fluctuates from 5 to 7.

Lacerta, The Lizard (September 25; MAPS 1 and 7)
In the no-man's land between Cygnus and Cassiopeia, and
hardly worth the trouble of locating.

Pegasus (October 1; MAP 7)
Heralder of autumn is the Great Square of Pegasus, a huge
rectangle formed in the sky by α, β, and γ Pegasi and α Andromedæ. It is, unfortunately, a rather sparsely-populated region.
π is a wide double (mags. 4·5, 6, distance 6′), but the only object
of real interest is β, an irregular variable ranging from mag. 2·2
to 2·8, with a rough period of about a month. With plenty of
comparison stars nearby (α Andromedæ (2·2), ε Pegasi (2·5),
α Pegasi (2·6), and γ Pegasi (2·9)) there is no excuse for not
keeping an eye on it.

Perseus (December 10; MAPS 1, 6 and 9)
A most glorious region between Auriga and Cassiopeia, boast-
ing probably the most dazzling fields visible to English observers. α is easily found by extending Andromeda's line, and
it lies at the centre of the compact group.
　Simply sweeping over Perseus is an experience, but in addition
there are some fine clusters; best of all is the famous 'double
cluster', half-way between α Persei and γ Cassiopeiæ. The two
groups are about equally rich, and both are larger than the
Moon. Choose a really dark night with Perseus in the zenith,
prop the binoculars really firmly, and gaze for several minutes
on end. Faint stars will slowly creep into view until the two
clusters are a mass of twinkling points.
　Rather more scattered is the loose cluster M.34, between β
Persei and γ Andromedæ. Which introduces β Persei itself, better
known by its Arabic name of Algol (the demon), because it
regularly fluctuates from mag. 2·3 to 3·7 and back again in a
period of 2 days 20 hours 49 minutes. It is the prototype of the
'dark-eclipsing' variable, where one star in the binary system is
large and dim, and periodically eclipses its companion. In
actual fact the stars are both considerably larger than the Sun,

and a mere three million miles separates their surfaces. The system is 60 light-years away.

Just south of Algol is ρ, an irregular variable (mag. 3·3 to 4·1, with no definite period).

57 Persei, towards Capella (α Aurigæ) is a pretty object: mags. 5 and 6, yellow and blue-white, distance 2'.

Pisces, The Fishes (October 25; MAPS 6 and 7)
A long, thin, and unsatisfactory constellation south of Andromeda; it marks the region of the sky where the ecliptic crosses the equator, going north, and the Sun therefore passes through it at the vernal equinox. It contains nothing of interest for binoculars.

Triangulum, The Triangle (November 25; MAP 6)
A small but obvious constellation (it really is triangular) between Andromeda and Aries. It has a variable, R (mag. 5·8 to 12·0, period 270 days).

Triangulum contains a curious object which gives rise to a strange paradox: it is so faint that it is more easily seen with binoculars than with a telescope! This is M.33, an external galaxy like M.31, approximately midway between α Arietis and β Andromedæ.

The reason lies in its size. Its apparent diameter is approximately the same as the Andromeda galaxy, but it is much fainter; and a telescope, which normally uses a much higher magnification than binoculars, enlarges it so much that it explodes into an invisible mist. Binoculars, with their lower magnification, have a better chance of success. Even so, the night must be exceptionally clear for there to be any chance at all; M.33 is about the most elusive telescopic object in the whole sky. There are actually records of naked-eye sightings when it was invisible with optical aid.

CHAPTER 10

Winter Stars

(Auriga, Camelopardus, Cancer, Canis Major, Canis Minor, Eridanus, Gemini, Lepus, Lynx, Monoceros, Orion, Taurus)

Auriga, The Charioteer (January 20; MAPS 1, 8 and 9)
Auriga is easily identified by its leading star, Capella, which shines between Gemini and Perseus with a distinctive yellow hue (it is in much the same physical state as the Sun). Lacking in binocular doubles, it contains two fine star-clusters, M.37 and M.38, both of which are easily picked up.

ε Aurigæ is an interesting star. It is one of the largest yet measured, with a diameter about equal to that of Saturn's orbit; yet in the true stellar tradition its mass is of the same order as that of the Sun. This means that the material composing it is very tenuous, and it is in no way comparable with a smaller, denser star. It also varies in brightness, from mag. 3·3 to 4·1, with the very long period of 27 years.

48 Aurigæ is a Cepheid variable: mag. 4·9 to 5·9, period 3 days 17 hours 30 minutes.

Camelopardus, The Giraffe (January 23; MAP 1)
Circumpolar, lying to the east of Cassiopeia. It is large and dim, virtually a hole in the sky with the naked eye and no more interesting in binoculars.

Cancer, The Crab (February 28; MAP 8)
Rather inconspicuous but easily found, lying midway between Regulus in Leo and Castor and Pollux in Gemini. Its two

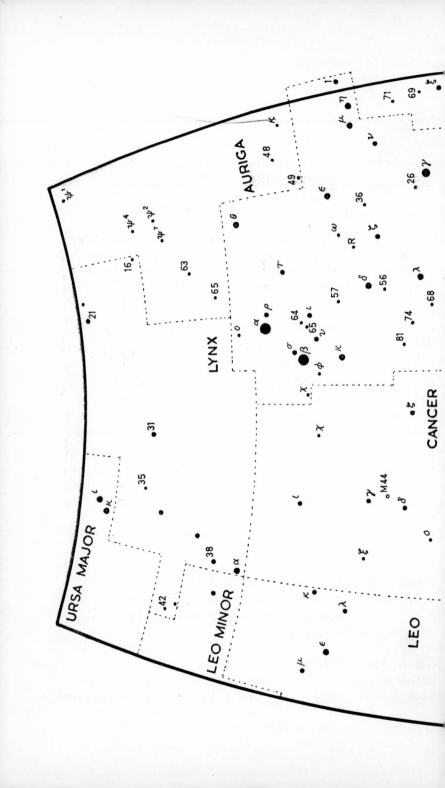

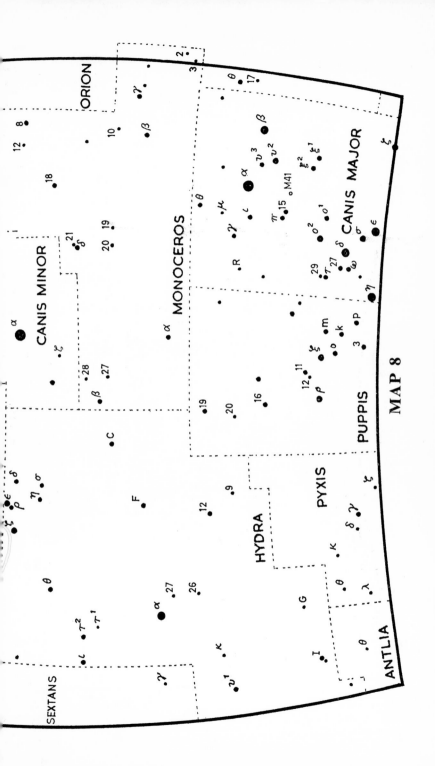

MAP 8

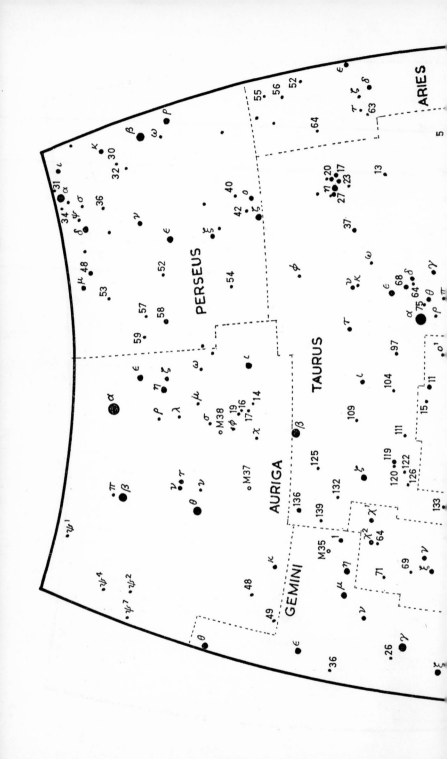

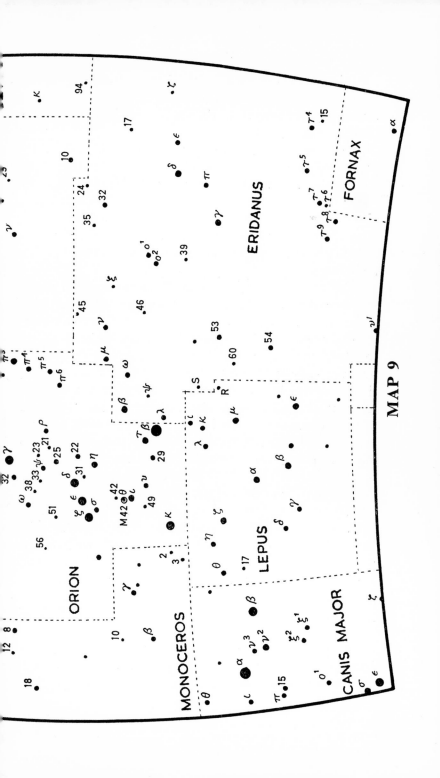

MAP 9

central stars, γ and δ, pinpoint the diffuse Præsepe cluster. It is so widely scattered that telescopically it is disappointing; the stars are spread beyond the edge of the field. Binoculars are the ideal instrument.

Cancer has a long-period variable, R; mag. 6·0 to 11·3, period 362 days. It is not difficult to find near maximum since it is equidistant from three stars in a rather empty field.

Canis Major, The Greater Dog (February 1; MAP 8)
A small bright constellation to the east of Orion. It is impossible to overlook since its leading star, Sirius, is the brightest in the whole sky.

Sirius betrays no secrets to small instruments, but in large telescopes it is seen to have a companion star; faint, and so close to the brilliant glare that it is difficult to see. This companion is of great interest, for it is what is known as a 'white dwarf' star. In far-off days—millions of years ago—it probably shone brightly, but now it has cooled and condensed into a planetary-sized body (slightly smaller than Neptune), at the same time retaining its original mass—about that of the Sun! This points to tremendous density, far beyond anything known on Earth; in fact a cubic inch of the white dwarf (known unofficially as the Pup, since Sirius is popularly called the Dog Star) would weigh many tons if it could be transported to the Earth's surface. Compare this with the diffuse, woolly state of a star such as ε Aurigæ.

The star μ, near Sirius, is an attractive triple in binoculars, and slightly south-east, near δ, there is a rich region. On the way pause and look at M.41, a bright cluster which is actually visible to the naked eye. It has a reddish star near the centre.

The variable R is worth looking up. It is an Algolid, with a period of only 27½ hours. The magnitude range is from 5·9 to 6·7.

Canis Minor, The Lesser Dog (February 15; MAP 8)
Like its larger brother it is distinguished by its leading star, the yellow Procyon, forming a triangle with Sirius and Orion's Betelgeuse. It contains no objects of interest.

Eridanus (December 10; MAPS 6 and 9)
Wanders through the region between Orion and Cetus, and is very barren. Its leading star, Achernar, marks its source—in Dec. $-57°$!

Gemini, The Twins (February 5; MAPS 8 and 9)
The two main stars in Gemini, Castor (α) and Pollux (β), shine distinctively to the north of Procyon. Castor, though appearing quite ordinary with binoculars, can be resolved telescopically into a close double star. This is a real binary system, the pair having a period of about 350 years. What is more amazing, each of the components is itself double; and to complete the miracle a third star, rather fainter and more distant, is also connected with the system and is double again! Castor therefore consists of six stars whose origin poses a leading celestial problem.

ζ Geminorum is interesting; a wide double, mags. 4 and 7, distance $1\frac{1}{2}'$, colours yellow and blue respectively. The primary is a Cepheid, varying from mag. 3·7 to 4·5 in a period of 10 days 3 hours 45 minutes. Two other variables are η, 3·2 to 4·2, period 230 days; and, much more elusive, R, 5·9 to 13·8, period 370 days, which like many long-period variables is visible only near maximum.

Investigate M.35, north-west of η. Even binoculars will reveal it as a wonderful star-flung object.

Lepus, The Hare (January 15; MAP 9)
A small bright constellation, very easily found since it is directly south of Orion. γ is an attractive double: mags. 3·8 and 6·4, distance $1\frac{1}{2}'$, yellow and red.

R Leporis, in an extended line from α through μ, is one of the reddest stars known. In addition it is a variable, mag. 6 to 10·4, period 420 days.

Lynx (February 19; MAPS 1 and 8)
Straggles across the vacancy between Ursa Major and Gemini; a very dull region.

Monoceros, The Unicorn (February 5; MAPS 8 and 9)

The main bulk of the constellation lies between Procyon and Sirius, but its interesting objects are confined to the region between Procyon and Betelgeuse. There is a fine cluster around the star 12 (H.VII.2 in Sir William Herschel's monumental catalogue of 2,500 objects, completed in 1802); and the variable 15 Monocerotis (mag. 4·9 to 5·4, period $3\frac{1}{2}$ days) is situated at the centre of another rather fainter cluster.

There are many splendid star-fields in this region, and it is unfortunate for English observers that it is always so low in the sky. On a transparent frosty night it is well worth sweeping at random.

Orion, The Hunter (January 15; MAP 9)

Undoubtedly the grandest constellation of all, containing in its core no less than seven stars brighter than the second magnitude. It is fitting that Nature should have placed her prize piece of handiwork across the celestial equator (the westerly belt star δ is almost exactly on the line), so that it can be seen from all parts of the globe.

Good sweeping can be had all over Orion, for it borders on a rich part of the Milky Way. But oddly enough there is a lack of binocular doubles; δ (mags. 2 and 6·8, distance 52″) is the best, but it is both difficult and unspectacular. δ itself is very slightly variable.

For one of the best-known variables in the sky look at Orion's top left-hand shoulder: the red star α, Betelgeuse. Not only is it bright, but it is strangely irregular. The range is from zero magnitude to about 1·1, or even fainter; records have also occasionally placed it above Capella (α Aurigæ) or even above Rigel. Rigel (β), marking the Hunter's right knee, is an intense blue-white, which unfortunately makes comparison difficult. Presumably Betelgeuse was brighter than Rigel when Bayer drew up his catalogue, since its variability was detected only a century ago.

Orion's prime wonder is its nebula, due south of the belt. It is so obvious to the naked eye that it is hard to explain how it went unnoticed until 1618.

Winter Stars

The Orion nebula, or by Messier's reckoning M.42, is a genuine mass of glowing gas inside our Galaxy; it is a mere thousand light-years away, which is near on cosmic reckoning, and it is about 15 light-years across. In a telescope, or even with good binoculars, it appears as a convoluted haze shining with a pale green hue. Projected against the brightest part is a mass of much dimmer gas, and the stars glowing in its interior add to the effect. With a large aperture it is a wonderful object, especially with the famous quadruple star θ Orionis embedded in the brightest part.

It now seems likely that much of Orion is a genuine star-cluster seen from close quarters; long-exposure photography has proved that the nebula we see with the eye is really only the nucleus of a colossal area of tenuous haze spread over hundreds of square degrees.

Taurus, The Bull (January 1; MAP 9)
Easily found by α, Aldebaran, which is met by prolonging Orion's belt upwards. Aldebaran, or rather its region, is interesting; it appears in the middle of a very scattered cluster, the Hyades. In actual fact it has no physical connection with the cluster, and it is perhaps misleading to define the Hyades as a cluster at all; they are so widespread that even binoculars are too powerful to compress them into anything spectacular.

The other naked-eye group in Taurus, the Pleiades, is much more remarkable. The naked eye shows a tiny collection of stars to the north-west of Aldebaran; in a good sky seven are seen, while some super-eyes can see twelve or more. Binoculars immediately add to the number, and the cluster is worth drawing.

τ Tauri, north of Aldebaran, is worth looking at: mags. 4 and 7, distance 1′, white and blue. λ Tauri is an Algolid variable, varying from mag. 3·4 to 4·3 in a period of 3 days 22 hours 52 minutes.

CHAPTER 11

The Heavens Open

Astronomical writers are apt to be influenced by their subject. When dealing with binocular observation they are encouragingly optimistic; when they reach the chapter on telescopes they point out that for anyone wanting to take up astronomy seriously, a reasonable telescope is essential. What is the truth?

The truth is that both have their advantages. First of all, binoculars are useless for observing planets, faint variable stars, and any but the widest double-stars—in fact, anything requiring light-grasp and high magnification. On the other hand they are ideal for sweeping up bright comets, watching trains left by fireballs, gauging auroræ, and observing the Milky Way and star-fields on a small scale. They can also be used, in conjunction with the naked eye, for following bright irregular variables; and if the sky is really well known they can help in searching for novæ.

In this materialistic and specialized age astronomy is following, however slowly, the general trend of modern science; and the expensive equipment of some workers is blinding others into thinking that their modest efforts are useless. It is of course true that in many fields the amateur simply cannot compete with the professional. But in astronomy there is a world of difference between the average professional, who is probably more adept at handling a calculating-machine than a telescope and who is unlikely to know whether Jupiter is north or south of the equator, and the amateur who patiently watches Betelgeuse brighten and fade in its secular majesty. One interprets, the other observes. And meteors, to take another case; if radar has partially displaced the visual observer, no electric circuit will ever evaluate the beauty of a fireball splintering the night sky in a flash of light.

The core of the matter is that if someone wants to observe, he *will*—despite all obstacles. There is a brigade of amateurs owning 6-inch telescopes who sit back and do nothing because they feel that there is nothing for them to do. This is criminal nonsense, and shows that their hearts are not in the subject. If someone is not willing to make the most of his equipment, then he will never make an observer.

This is where binoculars come in. Every amateur, no matter what his field, should know the night sky—and binoculars are ideal, for they will sweep among the stars much more quickly than anything larger. If, on the other hand, someone is given a large telescope, he will consider it rather *infra dig* to bother about so elementary a matter. He will flash his instrument from planet to planet, from the Moon to a double star, and finish up by deciding that there is so much to look at that it is not worth starting. Whereas the person who has spent a year getting to know the sky intimately will already have a sobering background. He will understand what there is to look at, and what can be usefully studied; he will possess judgment as an observer. A cathedral cannot be designed without some basic knowledge of architecture.

Another protest that might be voiced is that within the limited field of research open to binoculars there are already more than sufficient observers to cover all the possible avenues. This can be faulted for two reasons. First, no observer is perfect; if the mean is taken from a large number of results it is likely to be more accurate. Second, there are not nearly as many active observers as most people seem to think. Owning a telescope makes no-one an astronomer by itself; and considering the hundreds of excellent instruments that are scattered over the British Isles, it is dismal to reflect that only one per cent are used anything like regularly.

There are not enough good observers; this is an established

fact. Anyone who makes naked-eye observations of the bright variables, meteor showers, and auroræ, or who follows any new comets, can be doing really valuable work.

Of course it would be idle to suggest that no observer should want a proper telescope; there are many fields where a powerful instrument is essential. But equally there are several lines of research where a big telescope is completely useless. If these are apparently less romantic, remember that they are no less important. Astronomy is far too big a science to become overcrowded, and all that is needed in order to become an astronomer is that rare commodity: patience.

Index

Index

Index

145

Index